WORDS APART

WORDS APART

Losing your hearing as an adult

LESLEY JONES

JIM KYLE

PETER WOOD

Tavistock Publications
London and New York

First published in 1987 by
Tavistock Publications Ltd
11 New Fetter Lane, London EC4P 4EE

Published in the USA by
Tavistock Publications
in association with Methuen, Inc.
29 West 35th Street, New York NY 10001

Printed in Great Britain by T. J. Press (Padstow) Ltd, Padstow, Cornwall

British Library Cataloguing in Publication Data
Jones, L.
    Words apart: losing your hearing as an
    adult.
    1. Hearing impaired —— Rehabilitation
    I. title   II. Kyle, J.   III. Wood, Peter L.
    362.4'28   HV2395
    ISBN 0–422–60970–6

Library of Congress Cataloging in Publication Data
Jones, Lesley, 1947–
    Words apart: losing your hearing as an
    adult.
    Bibliography: p.
    Includes index.
    1. Deafness —— Social aspects.   I. Kyle, J. (James)
II. Wood, Peter L., 1940–   .   III. Title.
RF291.J63   1987   362.4'2   87–17966
ISBN 0–422–60970–6

Contents

PART IV   PUTTING IT ALL TOGETHER

Acknowledgements

Considerable thanks are due to all those who participated in the study, giving their time freely and making us welcome in their homes. They talked honestly about things that were not always easy to talk about and many of them spoke of wanting to help other people in the same situation as themselves. We can only hope that this book goes some small way to doing that. The research was funded by the Leverhulme Trust.

The other major debt of gratitude is owed to the secretaries on the project. Margaret Binnie typed endless transcripts and kept us going through the bad preparation times, as well as being responsible for the final presentation. Kaz Threlfall arranged the interviews and prepared all the early protocols and was more artistically inclined than any of us at drawing the figures. Eileen Nash, Betty Tracey, and Liz Young all helped at the final stage with efficiency and good humour.

Without these two groups of people, there would not have been a book. Thank you.

Introduction

It's easy to understand the loss of communication. Just watch hearing people talk to each other on a station platform 'through' the window of a train, and the variety of expressions and strategies will be astonishing. Usually the conversation begins in an animated way, a continuation of the conversation before the traveller boarded the train. Then the person outside begins to look embarrassed as the traveller understands so little of what is being said. The traveller starts to shout but stops because it disturbs people inside. They are left stranded in mutual incomprehension. One possibility is to become more and more visual using signs and gestures until both sides give up and laugh. The other possibility is to retire into embarrassed smiles and leave early, before the train has moved off. Communication has broken down completely or is reduced to wan smiles and an uncomfortable feeling. It takes a rare extrovert who does not mind persevering to keep a conversation going in the face of that amount of difficulty especially with everyone else in the train watching. This is hearing loss.

This must be one of the few occasions when hearing people actually experience what it is like to become hearing-impaired, and understand what it feels like to try to communicate in hearing loss. Personal relationships can follow these patterns of station conversation. People fall back on limited conversation and weak smiles and retire from any real communication, embarrassed by their own inadequacies and the eyes of other people upon them. People in relationships try to keep going, not necessarily communicating well but persevering just to maintain the relation. This book is about exactly these situations.

There is considerable medical literature on the cause, measurement, and clinical remediation of hearing loss but virtually nothing on the social effects. There are personal accounts in the literature, but

1

nothing on the process of becoming hearing-impaired – what actually happens, what it feels like, what sort of changes occur in everyday life and how people cope with them. The few reported studies are difficult to compare because of the use of samples of differing age and hearing loss. Studies are narrowed further by taking samples only from audiology clinics.

We set out to talk to both the adults who have become hearing-impaired and to the people at home, their partners, friends, flat-mates, and family. Our aim was to produce an account of value to those people themselves, and to those working in the field of hearing loss. We have interviewed people at different stages of loss in order to understand the whole process of becoming hearing-impaired. We have included two elements not previously examined. First we talked to a pre-diagnostic group. This consisted of people who had experienced discomfort with their hearing but who had had little or no contact with the audiological services. These are part of the three-quarters of the population of people discovered to have a significant hearing loss by the National Study of Hearing, who do not obtain hearing aids. These are the people who may attend occupational health clinics regularly to have their ears syringed but who for the most part deny that they have a problem. They are a hidden group in statistics on hearing loss.

Our second element was a return visit to a proportion of the informants. This group were amongst those who had most recently been diagnosed as having a hearing loss. By talking to them insight was gained on adjustment in the period immediately after the provision of a hearing aid.

We have combined both quantitative and qualitative methods of analysis. Information was collected with questionnaires, in transcripts of open-ended discussions, and by asking people to perform simple tasks. The use of this multi-faceted method produced a great deal of data, of which a proportion is reported. We have combined a psychological model of the process of adjustment with what the process actually feels like and the sense participants make of their situation.

Part I reviews the background literature. Chapter 1 looks at newer theories about disability and the idea of disability as a socially created problem. Chapter 2 is a straightforward review of the literature on hearing loss. Chapter 3 presents theories of illness behaviour and studies of the family including those where one person is disabled. Chapter 4 focuses on recent theories of adjustment. It is a first attempt to construct a theory of the process of hearing loss incorporating its personal and social effects. It is more technical and may prove more difficult for the reader but we believe it is an important step to take in understanding hearing loss. The theory is extended in Chapter 13. This section can be used as reference on hearing loss, disability, illness behaviour, the family, and adjustment.

Part II presents the findings of a research study of 123 people with a hearing impairment, and the people they live with. Chapter 5 describes the study in detail. Chapter 6 discusses the results of questions about home life and Chapter 7 about social and work life. Chapter 8 looks at the changes that occurred in the return visits to a group of the interviewees and at the process of change in coping with hearing loss. In this section, the material presented is mainly quantitative.

Part III concentrates on personal accounts of hearing loss and presenting the qualitative data. Chapter 9 is mainly about what it feels like to live with a hearing loss, how it is diagnosed or explained, and what sense is made of the label 'hard-of-hearing' or 'deaf'. Chapter 10 looks at living with other people in a hearing world. It discusses relationships with children, noise in the home, and what everyday life is like – the mechanics of everyday living. Chapter 11 contains the spectograms of 'family sculptures', how people saw themselves in the family before and after the hearing loss. Techniques used in family and dramatherapy have been adapted here for research purposes; this is a new element in research in this area. Chapter 12 is the account by one of the authors of the research from his perspective as a deafened researcher.

In *Part IV*, Chapter 13 proposes a psychological model of adjustment to acquired hearing loss and is an examination of theory in the light of our study and an attempt to offer a framework for the future study of acquired hearing loss. Chapter 14 discusses the process of hearing loss, the way in which hearing people might change in order to be effective for the hearing-impaired person, and how people themselves might change to cope with their hearing loss.

The concern of this book is those people who suffer a hearing loss in adult life, after puberty. The term hearing-impaired is used as a general term for this group. 'Deaf' is used for the prelingually deaf population. Hard-of-hearing we take to refer to a mild-to-severe loss occurring in adult life. 'Deafened' is used to describe those people suffering a profound hearing loss in the same period. It is vital to distinguish in this way between people who have had a hearing loss since birth or early childhood, and those who acquire it later in life.

The great majority of the people in this book have a mild to moderate hearing loss but it is a recognized and diagnosed loss which is affecting their lives. They are talked about as the people who are hearing-impaired or hard-of-hearing and in particular cases as the people who are 'deafened'.

The aim of the book is to look for positive ideas on how hearing people might change in order to be effective for the hearing-impaired person as well as to examine how people themselves cope with their hearing loss. The person is not in isolation but exists in the context of relationships. Social interaction is central to any response to hearing loss and it is this element which is the main concern of this book.

I

RELEVANT THEORIES

The changing concept of disability

By choosing the designs they did for a new set of stamps to commemorate the International Year of Disabled People in 1981, the Post Office unwittingly reflected society's conception of disability. The first most striking feature of the set of four stamps was that they had no full pictures of people. They did not appear, or were cut off at the wrist or waist. When one thinks that the year specifically included the word 'people' in its title, this was a major blunder. In addition, all the chosen symbols were stigmatizing, i.e. they showed the features which most clearly, in society's eyes, separated the handicapped from normality. There were wheelchairs for physical handicap, guide dogs for the blind and fingerspelling, disembodied hands for deaf people. If challenged about this image of disability, the graphic artists might have replied with another question, 'Well, how could we symbolize disability?'

It is this public image of disability which has proved most difficult for society to come to terms with throughout history. It is perhaps a most vexing question for us to deal with at this early stage. How *can* we describe disability without highlighting the problems people have and without specifying the aids and badges society has provided for them? Additionally, how do we come to terms with the fact that any stereotype will apply only partially to any single member of the population of people who are disabled.

THE PROGRESS OF DISABILITY

Thomas (1982) presents a brief effective historical account of disability, and it is possible to see the gradual alteration in society's response to people with problems. In the middle ages impairment, especially physical impairment, was attributed to supernatural causes, however, the view which has emerged in the west over the last few hundred years has emphasized the person and the handicap which the *individual* has to bear. What is still lacking is insight into this change and recognition of the likelihood that, since it occurs as a result of changes in society over time, the disability itself is as much a result of social conditions as of the individual.

Finkelstein (1980) suggests that there have been three phases from pre-industrial times through to the present time. It is the most recent which he considers to be acceptable to disabled people. In the earliest European feudal societies with a fixed social order it was possible for the 'cripple' to have a place and often a meaningful place. Thomas (1982) refers to it as a pre-industrial period during which the village idiot, whilst being ridiculed, was still taken care of and was a member of society. In a second, later phase in late-nineteenth-century industrial society in Britain, the situation of the handicapped became more visible. No work meant no standing and no money. Care was provided instead of participation and care took place by segregation. The idea of British Victorian charity was often to help the disabled but, in order to do so, it removed them from participation in society. People with an impairment were separated from society.

In the most recent phase, disabled people have emerged to demand their civil rights, to state their readiness for integration, and to begin to shape a new identity. This identity can be seen clearly in Campling's (1981) collection of writing where women who are disabled talk about not only the search for a place in society but also the desire for recognition of their own 'disabled culture'.

In many respects this outline is far too simplistic and, more importantly, functions only in a simple dimension – that of the individual. When Thomas (1982) invokes Berger and Luckman's (1966) idea of marginality in society's reality, he probably comes closest to a real understanding of the position of people with a disability. Even in achieving the integrationist's goal, they will become marginalized, classified to the periphery of social interaction, and thereby become acceptable because they do not affect life. It is, perhaps, this social view which needs to be explored most in seeing the development of disability.

TOWARDS A DEFINITION OF DISABILITY

We should try to make a number of terms less ambiguous. These include:

Impairment – the physical characteristics of the problem (e.g. the hearing loss measured by audiometric testing).

Disability – the restriction on activity caused by the impairment.

Handicap – the extent to which people are prevented from doing things and taking part in society (e.g. losing a job because of not being able to use the telephone). However, this can only be taken as a starting point from which to move on to explore more of the development of the concept of disability.

In an attempt to arrive at an adequate definition of disability, Blaxter (1976) emphasizes that like other ambiguous concepts such as health and sickness, disability and normality must be viewed as a continuum, so that the position of any individual on this continuum is dependent on a wide range of social and environmental factors. 'The disabled' are a group which society considers need help and as a result has provided a network of supportive services. Townsend (1973) also raises the question of how to define disability from a medical perspective:

> What do we mean when we say someone is disabled? First, there is the anatomical, physiological or psychological abnormality or loss. Thus we think of the disabled as people who have lost a limb or part of the nervous system through surgery, or in an accident, become blind or deaf or paralysed, or are physically damaged or abnormal in some particular, usually observable respect. Secondly, there are chronic clinical conditions altering or interrupting normal physiological or psychological processes, such as bronchitis, arthritis, tuberculosis, epilepsy, schizophrenia and manic depression. (109)

In this we see the problem attributed to the individual and arising in observable, diagnosable, testable loss. To this definition was added a clarification in that although the loss of a limb or other condition such as deafness may occur without illness, a disease, especially of long standing, may co-occur with a physical effect. To this extent, as in hearing loss arising through persistent and repeated infection of the middle ear, the two types defined by Townsend have a tendency to merge. Another report, by Jeffreys *et al.* (1969), adopted a dual approach model. First, there is the medical assessment model which identifies individuals who lack part or all of a limb, or who have a defective limb, organ or mechanism of the body. This model is usually the basis of an assessment on behalf of the state or other agencies. Each agency possesses strict criteria and guidelines as to what constitutes a specific disability. In some cases the identification of a condition is sufficient, whereas in others, where the implications are somewhat more ambiguous, a detailed and searching assessment may be necessary. The second approach requires the making of a value judgement as to what constitutes 'normality', insofar as an attempt is made to determine what a person of a particular age, sex, and vocational background should be able to achieve in their everyday life. An inability to successfully carry out this range of determined activities, leads to a classification of 'disabled'. As the report states: 'The emphasis, in short, is on the activities which the individual is unable to perform rather than on the underlying physical impairment or deficiency itself. The latter, indeed, may sometimes be inferred rather than demonstrated' (Jeffreys *et al*, 1969: 303–4). With definitions such as these, it is important to know *why* they have been developed. Those definitions used by the state are often for the purposes of awarding benefits such as invalidity, mobility and attendance allowances. They may therefore be geared towards performance in the labour market and secondly towards optimum performance to avoid the perception of 'malingering'. Harris, Cox, and Smith (1971) also attempt to distinguish between the concepts 'impaired', 'disabled', and 'handicapped' by defining their extent physically and also the implications deriving from them, so as to avoid the ambiguities that often arose in the past. They consider that:

> Impairment has been defined as lacking part or all of a limb, or having a defective limb, organ or mechanism of the body. Disablement is the loss or reduction of functional ability. Handicap is the disadvantage or restriction of activity caused by disability. (2–3)

The limitation of this approach lies in its emphasis on the practical implications of handicap, which although applicable to the case of impaired mobility appears far less relevant in areas of sensory deprivation such as deafness, where the effect may be on personal, family, social, and vocational relationships. Davis (1983), however, adapted Harris, Cox, and Smith's scheme and applied it specifically to auditory dysfunction (Table 1.1). The difference here becomes immediately apparent in that psychological and societal implications are recognized to be part of the disorder, impairment, disability, and handicap scheme.

But these views, plausible though they may be initially, are by no means universally held. On the one hand they are medical cure-based approaches, classificatory and isolating, and they require acquiescence

10

Table 1.1 Auditory dysfunction

	Disorder	Impairment	Disability	Handicap
Definition	Pathology of the hearing organ	Abnormality function of the auditory system	Reduced abilities of the individual	Need for extra effort, reduced independence
Area affected	Middle ear Inner ear Hair cells Auditory nerve Brainstem Auditory cortex	Auditory sensitivity Auditory discrimination Auditory localization Temporal processing Binaural integration Tinnitus	Speech perception Environmental awareness Orientation	Grade of employment Scope of employment Remuneration Personal relationships Social integration Anxiety, embarrassment
Appropriate remedial action		Medical and surgical treatment	Environmental and personal aids to hearing	Counselling and special provision

Adapted from Davis 1983.

and acknowledgement from the individual before treatment can occur. Tomlinson (1982) takes this issue further in relation to children:

> All over the world, powerful social groups are in the process of categorising and classifying weaker social groups and treating them unequally and differentially. The rationalisations and explanations which powerful groups offer for their actions differ from country to country and the ideologies supporting systems of categorisation differ. The notion that a variety of social groups are solely engaged in 'doing good' to the children they refer, assess, place and teach in special education is something of a rationalisation. ... They also have a very real power to define and affect the lives and fortunes of the children they deal with.(5)

McKnight (1981) makes this much more specific to the classifying professions in terms of the disabling effects they create:

> First is the translation of a need into a deficiency. A need could be understood as a condition, a want, a right, an obligation of another, an illusion or an unresolvable problem. Professional practice consistently defines a need as an unfortunate absence or emptiness in another.

Like the riddle of the half-full glass,

> The basic function of modernized professionalism is to legitimise human beings whose capacity is to see their neighbour as half-empty.(28)

> The second disabling characteristic of professionalised definitions of need is the professional practice of placing the perceived deficiency in the client. While most modernized professionals will agree that individual problems develop in a socio-economic-political context, their common remedial practice isolates the individual from the context. (28)

In relation to hearing loss, these criticisms are particularly powerful, since by its very nature hearing loss is potentially isolating. The rehabilitation process as defined by professionalism has to be understood in this social context. The influence of the professional definition of need is particularly persuasive in the provision in the UK.

In reviewing the provision of services within the UK in a historical context, Blaxter (1976) emphasizes a different dual approach that developed between voluntary and state efforts. The main characteristic of this approach has always been that,

> a division has existed between those 'outside' the economic system, to whom only charity is owed, and those who are economically active and potentially valuable, whom society must help in its own interests, and as a matter of social justice. (2)

The Beveridge Report of 1942 reiterated this dual distinction in that although it sought to ensure the freedom from want of all citizens, rehabilitation from handicap still possessed an economic dimension, in that it was seen as a process whereby the disabled became 'producers and earners'. This approach was subsequently reinforced by the National Insurance Act of 1946, and the Disabled Persons (Employment) Acts of 1944–8. The National Assistance Act of 1948 was somewhat broader in scope in that it contained a provision for those suffering from disability where their economic potential was non-existent, but there also emerges one reason for the seemingly rigid interpretation of disability. To categorize a particular person as 'disabled' may imply a qualification for state benefit or the payment of insurance compensation.

Even amongst voluntary organizations, there are often rigid classifications of individuals but often from different perspectives. Referring to studies of agencies for the blind in the USA by Scott (1966), Blaxter found that an excess of services for children, employable adults, and the totally blind existed, despite the fact that these categories were in a numerical minority in comparison with the partially blind, the elderly blind, and the multiply-handicapped. A similar situation can be seen to exist in voluntary organizations for the deaf in the UK, many of which have existed for over a hundred years. Despite the superficial impression given by the extensive use of the word 'deaf' both in their titles and literature, they have in almost all cases been orientated towards the provision of social work services and social facilities for the prelingually deaf signing community and have provided little in the way of facilities or support for the numerically much larger group who acquire a hearing loss as adults.

The medical diagnosis and treatment model may not therefore match either the expectations or the perceived needs and problems of a patient if it is to be related to state provision or to the system of categorization. For this reason there has been an increasing realization that a physical condition may often have important family, social, vocational, and psychological implications for the patient. Such a trend can be seen in the treatment of hearing loss in adults. In the past, ear, nose and throat and audiology clinics concerned themselves exclusively with either surgical intervention or the issue of hearing aids. The social implications were left entirely to the voluntary agencies that existed. It is only since 1978 that hearing therapists have begun to be trained within the National Health Service to deal with these problems of personal and social adjustment.

Nevertheless, these developments take us only part of the way to Finkelstein's (1980) third phase of equality for disabled people. The fact of past provision is no longer a convincing reason for maintaining particular attitudes towards disability.

THE ATTITUDINAL DIMENSION

Traces of Victorian sentimentality about disability still remain and these are perceived in 'exceptional' cases of people overcoming disability. Popular media delight in portraying the handicapped person struggling against the problem and by hard work, exceptional skill, or both, succeeding in defeating the handicap and being a notable member of society. The extent to which deeply held beliefs about disability have shaped the complex service provision outlined by Blaxter (1976) cannot be underestimated. At one extreme, we have the distancing effects of stereotyping and stigmatizing (arising in categorization) and at the other there is this need to create an atmosphere to allow positive evaluation of worth in all members of society. On another interacting dimension we have the attitudes of the disabled person.

Goffman's (1963) work on stigma attempted to understand the problems disabled people face in their personal relationships with the rest of society by conceiving of disability as a deviance from society's anticipated pattern, either physically or behaviourally. This deviance perceived to exist by both the person involved and the rest of society creates a sense of difference or stigma. Goffman used the term stigma to refer to: 'an attribute that is deeply discriminating, but it should be seen that a language of relationships, not attributes, is really needed' (1–4).

He went on to argue that a deviation from the norm, which occurred as a direct result of physical impairment and which isolated the sufferer, was part of some social process that created stigma in those people with a 'known record of, for example, mental disorders, imprisonment, addiction, alcoholism, homosexuality, unemployment, suicidal attempts and radical political behaviour'. Such an all-embracing approach, however, was criticized by Boswell, Jaehnig, and Mittler (1975) who pointed out that in the case of the physically handicapped 'their predicament removes the opportunity to choose whether to deviate or not'. Blaxter (1976) considered that the perception of stigma appeared to depend on the nature of the impairment and was 'strongest in all those conditions which threatened the taken-for-granted world of everyday interaction'. A limited range of mobility problems did not interfere with this process but any condition which made communication difficult and therefore interrupted interaction fell outside the range of what was acceptable. Blaxter's research found that, as a result of this, the people who felt most strongly that their disability was a stigma were those suffering from ataxias, spasticity, severe multisclerosis, deafness, blindness to a lesser extent, and epilepsy. The perception that stigma exists, however, can only arise as the result of experiences gained through the process of interacting with others, at home, with the family, socially, and vocationally. The ability to cope with a disability may vary within a given condition. Examples were cited by Blaxter where even when a severe mobility problem existed the sufferer had vehemently rejected the category of disabled, and of cases where the disability appeared only slight, but the person concerned felt that a whole change had occurred in their life pattern.

Nevertheless, it has been society's attitude which recent writers have criticized most (Thomas 1982, Finkelstein 1980). The inherent weakness in society's view has largely been recognized, and moves towards integration are widespread particularly in education. The situation in adult life is much more complex. Jobs are subject to economic realism: 'if the disability gets in the way of the job, we need to find another employee'. What has begun to be suggested is that it is the job which should change if disability occurs in adult life. And this is of necessity true if we are to achieve any measure of acceptance for disabled people.

The problems then can be predicted. We have in the UK a development away from the old categorization system in education, a greater belief in the rights of all people to participate, and a greater commitment to reform our provision of health care services to meet the demands of a different clientele. At the same time, the attitude shift required by society is only partly occurring and varies markedly according to which type of handicap is being discussed, so that we should probably still obtain the same results as Shears and Jensema (1969) if we were to evaluate the closeness of various disabled groups. A change has begun, but for the major part of the population acceptance is a long way off; equality is still over the horizon.

DISABILITY AND DEAFNESS

Where does this leave people with a hearing loss? The majority probably do not accept the term 'disabled' and are reluctant to apply for special concessionary fares on transport because of titles like 'Disabled Person's Rail Card' and because much of the publicity shows people in wheelchairs. They might be prepared to discuss the term 'handicapped' but with no real sense that it is a fair judgement of their situation. What might be agreed is that in having a hearing loss there is an impairment which causes difficulties personally and socially but since these do not threaten life or job directly they are problems to be coped with, not accepted as handicapping.

But the reality is that service provision, in education and health, treats hearing loss in the same way as any other problem. The truth may be that despite the long history of provision, hearing loss is one of the least understood disabling conditions. The likelihood is that not seeing the difficulties in hearing loss as anything more than personal adaptation, we hinder the actual process of understanding hearing loss. Deafness is peculiar in that it is social from the beginning. Whether it arises in infancy or later in life, suddenly or gradually, it strikes at the very heart of social interaction. The physical normality of hearing-impaired individuals simply heightens the sense of frustration and mistrust when communication does not work. Breakdown in communication simply produces an attribution of blame ('he's not listening') or distancing statements ('stupid old deafie') but in any case, a gap appears in which stereotypes arise.

'Deaf' is one of these. As Kyle (1985) points out, deafness is unfortunately not a single dimension. There are at least four subdivisions related to onset and severity. Those born with a hearing loss may be profoundly deaf or partially-hearing, and likely to use sign language, and those acquiring hearing loss may have profound or partial losses, with sudden or gradual onsets interacting with the degree of loss. In this book we are concerned with those who acquire a loss after the age of 16. There is already a considerable literature on prelingual deafness in education (Conrad 1979, Meadow 1980) and in society (Schein and Delk 1974, Kyle and Woll 1985) and it seems clear that there are grounds for seeing these people as a minority group with a separate emerging identity. From an initial work, Kyle and Wood (1983), it became clear that people who acquire a hearing loss have little in common with those who are prelingually deaf. The questions then begin to come into focus for those who acquire a hearing loss in adult life: does the impairment of hearing lead to disability or to handicap? Is there a pattern of hearing loss outcomes? Can these be seen independently of service provision and ultimately society's attitudes? What is the process of adjustment for people facing declining hearing? How can our understanding of this process enhance the effectiveness of the support we provide? How does acquired hearing loss relate to the more militant active groups of disabled people fighting for rights? It is to many of these questions that we address ourselves in the following sections of this book.

2

Hearing loss: psychological, social, and vocational effects

Two hundred years ago, Doctor Samuel Johnson called deafness the most desperate of human calamitites. It is still a desperate calamity. Deafness is not a killer but it is a destroyer. It destroys so much that is vital in our everyday lives. Relationships within the family, with friends and with those with whom we work are constantly under strain when there is a breakdown in easy communication. We are impatient and uncaring when sufferers misunderstand or seem outright dim. Rejection and isolation follow. (Harvington 1983: 1151)

Two hundred years on, and the story is still the same. Deafness casts a shadow on communicative life. Sadly, what we know now in research terms does not take us much further in changing the quality of life for those suffering from hearing loss. Hearing-aid technology does not solve all the problems, even when there is proper service delivery and backup. Although there may be hope for success in the case of cochlear implants (Loeb 1985) it seems unlikely that it will be appropriate for all with a hearing loss. Deafness can still be a desperate calamity. However, the nature of hearing loss, its causes, and its measurement, are not the subject to be explored here. There are already excellent and recent discussions of these topics (e.g. Thomas 1984 and Lysons 1984). What concerns us is the effect of the loss on psychological well-being. But first we need to discuss the nature of the population.

HEARING-IMPAIRED POPULATIONS

Despite the apparent simplicity of deciding whether a person can hear or not, it is in practice very difficult to specify what constitutes the hearing-impaired population. People who are born deaf represent a small minority of those with hearing loss and so it should be stated that we are dealing with those who *acquire* a hearing loss after the age of 16 years. We are concerned primarily with those still technically within their working lives, i.e. up to the age of 65. Depending on where the line is drawn in terms of severity of hearing loss, this can mean thousands or millions of people in the UK. Hearing-impairment is a major and common problem.

One recent estimate from the 1980 Health Interview Survey suggests 4.38 per cent have a hearing loss in the age group 17–64 years. Davis (1983), drawing on a more systematic survey in the UK (National Study of Hearing) where audiograms were taken, suggests there are more. Taking ten-year age groups 21–30 and so on up to 60 years, anything between 1 per cent and 23 per cent of the population have hearing losses greater than 25 decibels (that is the average taken from the ear with the better hearing level) and up to 6 per cent have losses greater than 45 decibels. In the UK this may mean a population of 10 million with significant hearing losses. Of these, only a quarter will have requested help or obtained a hearing aid (Haggard, Foster, and Iredale 1981).

These incidences of hearing loss are overwhelming and even though they represent comparatively mild losses they indicate problems in many situations where communication is vital. Not surprisingly, audiological services are not ready to deal with these proportions of the population. The typical pattern of diagnosis, referral, and hearing aid fitting is expensive in personnel and could not cope if all people with these measurable losses were to seek help. At the same time, the fact that so few people refer themselves for audiological help makes research study on representative populations very difficult, a point which we will explore shortly.

By and large, audiological provision agencies have been aware of their shortcomings (Watts 1983) and have begun to explore different models of providing health care for those with hearing loss. However, because the provision has been medical, the problem is defined in terms of diagnosis and delivery rather than management of hearing loss. What is of most concern is the sheer magnitude of the task. The prevalence of hearing loss in old age, and the fact that the population in the UK is gradually becoming older and living longer, poses major problems in dealing effectively with hearing loss and at the same time increases the pressure for action.

In viewing the research work available, there are great difficulties in

19

establishing comparability. Studies have almost all used audiology clinic attenders or volunteers. Both types of respondent are heavily weighted towards middle-class occupations and particularly towards professional and managerial classes. When Davis (1983) reported the survey data on hearing-aid ownership he showed that similar percentages of each socio-economic group had hearing aids, while according to hearing tests more than twice as many skilled and unskilled manual workers *should* have had hearing aids as compared to professional and managerial groups. The studies so far are therefore subject to 'hidden' social-class effects.

In addition, there are difficulties in separating out the different groups by age of onset and by age of respondent. Many studies have a disproportionate weighting towards elderly, retired people. While these people have important problems, their nature is different to those of younger people with young families, jobs, and still expanding social and financial expectations. Strangely, also, there is insufficient discrimination between prelingually deaf people and those who have acquired a loss. In studies prior to 1970, there was considerable vagueness about the distinction and often even a mixing of the two groups. This confusion does not help in understanding how hearing loss affects adult life. No study which we have examined adequately deals with all these difficulties.

HEARING AIDS

Following from the discussion so far, it is not surprising that an important area of research has been in the development and use of hearing aids. There have been major strides in the production of hearing aids and there are hopes for technological developments which will make them even more effective. However, hearing aids do not restore hearing and the adaptation task includes getting used to the hearing aid. We have therefore not focused on the technical aspects of the aid nor have we included a survey of hearing aids by type and function.

One feature of adjustment is whether or not the patient increases their use of the hearing aid satisfactorily. Superficially, the simplest thing to measure is whether or not the patient wears the aid. As has often been suspected, not everyone uses the aid with which they have been issued. Brooks (1972) suggests that nearly 70 per cent of people 'never' or 'only occasionally' use their hearing aid. Part of the problem seemed to be poor counselling and the type of aid issued (i.e. body-worn) and Stephens (1977) suggests that things can be improved by more extensive support such as exists in Denmark (Pedersen, Frankner, and Terkildsen 1974). However, when Brooks in 1979 and 1981 returned to measure more precisely hearing-aid use for post-aural aids, it was still true that much less use was made than was felt desirable by audiologists. What is interesting is that Brooks (1981) reported a decline in use over time. This is in contradiction with Hutton's (1983) detailed study in the USA but is supported by another small study made in the UK (Kyle, Wood, and Jones 1983). Only Haggard, Foster, and Iredale (1981) seem to provide a more optimistic view of people's capacities to judge their hearing-aid use and then to use them more appropriately.

The generally poor use of hearing aids is understandable from Thomas's (1984) finding that 42 per cent of his sample had little or no benefit from their aid when tested in speech discrimination tests. However, he did find that a proportion of people did persevere with their aids when they were getting no benefit. Kaplan (1985) maintains that many of these problems can be avoided by assessment of the patient prior to issue of the aid. Rupp, Higgins, and Maurer (1977) developed a scale for predicting hearing-aid use and claim that the key determining factor is motivation based on the individual feeling the need for help. The more accurate the estimate of their own hearing loss, the more effective will be their use of hearing aids (Maurer and Rupp 1979)

However, in some respects the actual amount of use is not as important as the type of use. Hutton (1983) reports much greater use in employed people than unemployed. This finding fits very well with that of Kyle and Wood (1984) who found less use at home than at work, even in the same people. Thomas's (1984) findings do not show a clear trend either way. However, hearing-aid use did seem to relate most to communication requirements and pressure. Where there was a noticeable public need such as at work, inconspicuous aids were used. Apart from specifying the need for more research into situations of use, the findings make it clear that adjustment to hearing-aid use is not simply a matter of wearing it more often. However, it is obvious that hearing-aid use is not the whole story.

HEARING LOSS: PSYCHOLOGICAL EFFECTS

Perhaps the most direct insights we have on deafness come from personal accounts. People frequently write about their deafness offering an inside picture. Jack Ashley's (1985) personal account of his sudden deafness is well known: 'But I was painfully and permanently aware of what I had lost. My perception of that loss is a lifelong burden' (61). Sudden deafness often produces a very negative personal feeling but even when deafness is gradual it can still provoke these strong feelings: 'First thing every morning I would drum my fingers on the bedside table to see if I could still hear the sound before I put on my aid. There's no need to do that now and it really doesn't matter any more. I'm there – on that "other side", deaf' (Cooke 1984: 36). As a psychologist herself, Cox (1985) can stand back from the problems of deteriorating hearing: 'Personal pressure to deny the difficulty is considerable, as the feelings of normality which we take for granted are undermined and with that goes the loss of status we have come to expect as being treated as a normal healthy person' (3).

These accounts are perhaps most illustrative when taken together and balanced against the differing factors which can affect the individual. We will aim to bring out many of these features in later sections of our own data. But there are other research studies to examine.

The effect of a sudden hearing loss has been described by Lehman (1954) as 'one of life's most terrifying experiences' and, writing in a handbook for social workers with the deaf, Peck, Samuelson, and Lehma (1926) considered that 'everybody who acquires deafness goes through hell'. Even early work such as that of Kraepelin (1915) and Haines (1927) claimed to detect such disorders as delusions of persecution, suspicion, and a sense of isolation. Others, such as Menninger (1924), attempted to apply the newly developed psycho-analytical framework. Hunt (1944) wrote of the feeling of fear engendered in a person which created:

> Fear of failure, fear of ridicule, fear of people, fear of new situations, chance encounters, sudden noises, imagined sounds; fear of being slighted, avoided, made conspicuous; these are but a handful of fears that haunt the waking and even the sleeping hours of the sufferer from progressive deafness. (230–1)

Audiological casualties occurring during the Second World War gave research an impetus. Work with war-deafened soldiers enabled psychiatrists such as Knapp (1948) to obtain an insight into the effect of sudden hearing loss on the individual. Knapp considered that the most significant subjective response was loneliness coupled with a fear of social situations. People were anxious that the inability to communicate normally would be perceived by others as indicating stupidity. A whole constellation of somatic complaints were reported ranging from stress to tension headaches. A direct relation seemed to exist between the level of hearing loss involved and social-interaction problems. When the degree of hearing loss was profound, grossly abnormal facial expressions and mannerisms emerged and, with lip-reading providing only superficial help, attempts to maintain social bonds sometimes hardly seemed worthwhile. Knapp considered a healthy personality prior to hearing loss meant that the problems arising from a sudden hearing loss could often be managed without serious emotional problems. The compensatory and neurotic defences employed by the deafened bore a marked similarity to those with a more progressive loss outlined by Menninger (1924). Knapp listed these as:

1 *Overcompensation:* adopting an extrovert lifestyle and bonhomie, with great emphasis on talking, which of course presents no problem to the suddenly deafened and in addition alleviates the need to lip-read and understand the other person,
2 *Denial:* an attempt to lead a lifestyle as before, making no attempt at adjustment,
3 *Retreat from society:* many found that the problem of maintaining social interaction was so great that the effort was not worth it,
4 *Somatic complaints:* the emergence by neurotic displacement of a range of physical complaints,
5 *Exploitation:* the adoption of a badge of invalidism in order to gain and subsequently exploit sympathetic feelings in others.

However, Knapp's results are confounded by the presence of patients who may have suffered additional battlefield trauma in addition to their deafness. Ingalls' (1946) study is therefore of considerable interest as his sample included a majority who had not had any combat experience and where the hearing loss was of a more progressive nature. But for many of his group the loss had been present since childhood. Ingalls reported that neuroses detected were primarily of the anxiety type and that hysteria, depression, and psychosomatic symptoms were frequent complicating features.

Of far greater applicability was the work of Ramsdell (1962) who also had experience of treating Second World War veterans. It was Ramsdell's belief that the frequently encountered depressive reactions, subsequent to a hearing loss occurring, often resulted from the eradication of background noise at what he described as the 'primitive level of hearing'. This level of hearing was considered of importance in that it 'contributes to our sense of comfort by ever reassuring us that we are part of the living, ongoing world'. But researchers such as Thomas (1984) have claimed that such theories, 'while interesting, have no basis over and above their intuitive appeal'.

There have been several deprivation or simulation studies (e.g. Myerson 1948 and Leith 1972 a and b) but the interaction problems and irritability occurring are difficult to interpret since the subjects knew they could return to the hearing world. Looking directly at personality, Welles (1932) gave the Bernreuter Personality Inventory (a standard personality test) to paired groups of hard-of-hearing subjects and hearing acquaintances of the same sex and similar demographic characteristics. Female subjects dominated with 87 per cent of the hard-of-hearing and 89 per cent of the control group. Welles found that the hard-of-hearing showed only slightly more introversion, submissiveness, and emotionality than normal, and where subjects had achieved a degree of adjustment and success in their everyday life in spite of their hearing loss, no difference from the control group was found to exist. However, Barker *et al.* (1953) considered that not enough effort had been made to eliminate from the inventory questions which were confusing or ambiguous in the case of deaf subjects, and Thomas (1984) claimed the sample was unlikely to be representative, not only because of the low response rate and massive sex bias, but also because few hearing-impaired people join societies for the hard-of-hearing from where the subjects came. Nett (1960) attempted to identify the social, psychological, and vocational handicap resulting from a hearing loss utilizing two measures: the WAIS (Wechsler Adult Intelligence Scale) and the MMPI (Minnesota Multiphasic Personality Inventory). The population interviewed was drawn from audiology-clinic records of people having been referred either by their medical practitioner or by themselves. The level of hearing loss was mild in 43 per cent of the subjects (mean loss 29dB or less). Some 20 per cent were outside the normal range on the MMPI but Thomas (1984) severely criticized the statistical basis of the finding.

Levine (1960), in previous research to formulate a policy for rehabilitation, included both congenital and acquired hearing loss. She claimed that the major factor affecting psychological reaction to acquired deafness is the stability of the personality at the time of onset. But she also included the nature and effect of physical damage; the impact on the person's lifestyle and the attitude of family and society in general as other factors. Levine emphasized that where a person previously had an active social life as part of the hearing community, then society's ambivalent and often negative reaction is only too readily apparent. The reaction can be traumatic and create feelings of despair, panic, rage, or worthlessness, depending on the personality of the person affected. The failure to interact successfully either leads to psychic detachment or irritable, hostile hypersensitivity. It is interesting to note that Zeckel (1950) considers that where neurotic defences have become apparent in a person with acquired deafness, it was often the case that the neurosis existed before hearing was lost, and that the less neurotic the person was, the better he or she would adapt to deafness. Myklebust (1964), too, found significant variables in the age of hearing-loss onset, the degree of hearing loss, and the subject's sex. It was found that those subjects whose hearing loss had occurred early in life showed the greatest emotional deviation. Male subjects showed a greater incidence of personality disorder.

Meadow-Orlans (1985) also made the same claim about time of onset as if this was a finite point in time. However, Kyle and Wood (1983), and we suspect many others, have found people very unreliable in their estimates of onset *and*, since their losses are usually gradual, more likely to be referring to a long period of years as the time of onset.

The attempt to detect the presence of psychiatric symptoms in relationship to hearing loss was continued by Mahapatra (1974 a and b) using a sample of eighty-nine otosclerotic patients consecutively admitted to the ENT ward of a hospital for stapedectomy. Prior to surgery, the experimental group of bilaterally-impaired, and a control group of unilaterally-impaired patients, completed an interview and the Cornell Index, an inventory used for psychiatric screening. The difference between groups was found to be statistically significant and overall female subjects scored significantly higher than males. The findings of the Cornell Index score were confirmed by the psychiatric interview that followed. Stephens (1980), using the Eysenck Personality Inventory and the Crown–Crisp Experimental Index on 353 patients attending an audiology unit, found the group to manifest introversion and neurosis in comparison with the normal population. Cooper (1978) was concerned with mythical concepts such as 'the deaf' in which all categories of acquired hearing loss come within a common definition, and resulting ideas such as 'the deaf are paranoid'. His survey of past research showed its contradictory nature.

25

Ramsdell (1962) and Denmark (1969) had detected the presence of morbid suspiciousness and hostility of occasional psychotic intensity. Ingalls (1946) and Knapp (1948), however, had found paranoid reactions extremely rare. Cooper's main criticism centred on the need to differentiate hearing-loss categories and establish the time of onset when assessing possible psychosis. Markides *et al.* (1979) felt that the inability to hear one's own speech when the hearing loss was severe or profound led to a degeneration of speech, especially a lack of precision in articulation. There was a tendency for the quality of speech to develop a monotonous tone. Cowie and Douglas-Cowie (1983) related this to age of onset. In addition difficulty was encountered in assessing the level of background noise so that a person would often either speak too loudly or too quietly. An increasing awareness of these difficulties could lead to withdrawal to avoid embarrassment. Markides *et al.* referred to the development of depression, discouragement, suspicion of friends and family, over-sensitivity, irritability, and sometimes an acute state of paranoia. But even so, these repeated claims about paranoid symptoms seem to be based on reworkings of the same research coupled with the same stereotypes of deafness. There is very little hard data.

A study by Thomas and Herbst (1980) of adults of employment age at least one year after hearing-aid issue made a more extensive analysis. As before, the sample came from hearing-aid clinics in London and consisted of 211 subjects (57 per cent male and 43 per cent female). The mean age for male subjects was 53 and for females 48 years. The categories of hearing loss were 59 per cent sensorineural, 27 per cent mixed, and 14 per cent conductive. Average hearing losses were for sensorineural 53dB, mixed 53dB, and conductive 57dB. Data collection included audiological testing, speech-discrimination testing, self-rating of hearing loss, questions on hearing loss, work, anxiety, family life, and general well-being. Of those tested 19 per cent were considered to be disturbed and a further 20 per cent in the intermediate category. Due to the presence of a social-class bias in the population towards the professional classes, the authors claimed that their figures may underestimate the degree of psychological disturbance.

In addition, it was found that for those subjects having a mean loss of 70dB or more the incidence of psychological disturbance was found to be substantially greater. But there was no evidence of the suspiciousness that Markides *et al.* (1979) reported. When utilizing the speech-discrimination scores in relation to the degree of hearing loss it was found that the incidence of psychological disturbance 'increases dramatically for those who have a severe loss compounded by poor speech discrimination'. An ambiguity was found, however, to exist in that those with poor speech-discrimination scores but with a mild or moderate hearing loss manifested a much lower incidence of psychological disturbance than those with a hearing loss in excess of 70dB. A relationship was established between the presence of hearing loss and a generally detrimental effect on the general health and sense of well-being of the subjects.

One of the major difficulties of such research was recognized by Thomas (1984) in that it was difficult to obtain insights into the handicapping nature of hearing loss. He considered that; 'In other words, the study served the actuarial purpose of quantifying psychological disturbance without throwing any light on what it was about living with hearing loss, which predisposed the sufferers to become psychologically disturbed' (96).

Thomas's second study of those with sensorineural hearing loss examined further the extent of psychological disturbance. With eighty-eight subjects of employment age from hearing-aid clinics with sensorineural losses of 60dB or greater, Thomas (1984) showed that basic personality structure was not affected by hearing loss, thus contradicting nearly all the earlier findings. However, whereas in Thomas's first study those suffering both a severe hearing loss and poor speech discrimination also suffered a high likelihood of psychological disturbance, this phenomenon did not manifest itself in the second study. In addition, psychological disturbance was not found to be related to age, sex, social class, or mean hearing loss. A finding that confirmed earlier suggestions that sudden traumatic loss offered a better adjustment potentiality than a progressive loss applied to twelve subjects, all of whom had suffered this type of hearing loss, and none of whom were psychologically disturbed. Thomas summed up: 'although severe hearing loss was not associated with a very high level of psychological disturbance as in the first study, hearing-impaired adults were still nearly four times more likely to be psychologically disturbed than were normal healthy people'(125). The psychological disorders existed at the 'psychoneurotic' level and did not result in 'obviously abnormal behaviour, as is the case with most forms of personality disorder'.

A far more difficult outcome to identify is stress, not least because of its presence in most people's lives. It is difficult to determine whether chronic stress is a cause of psychological problems or an outcome. In considering this problem Stone (1985) suggested that:

> much depends upon how the stressor (hearing loss) is perceived and what the response to it is. When a major life crisis is seen as a challenge, coping is within reach. When the same life event is perceived as a crushing blow, helplessness and depression negate effective coping. (Stone 1985)

Whilst agreeing that all people suffer stress occasionally Trychin (1985) nevertheless considered that as a group the hearing-impaired may well experience more stress than hearing people. In an article concerned with stress control he maintained that as stress could be considered to manifest itself as tension, pressure, anxiety and worry there is both a physical and psychological dimension.

As regards the hearing impaired:

> the most frequent and intense stress results from process problems in communication – the mechanics, rather than the content of communication. Noisy backgrounds, talking with more than one person at a time, the unavailability of telephone amplification devices, and interference produced by tinnitus are just a few examples of common process problems for hard of hearing people. (Trychin 1985: 8)

The problem remains, however, of identifying those aspects of hearing loss that produce stress rather than being manifestations of personality problems.

The whole area is bedevilled by the well-established arguments about the measurement of psychiatric morbidity. From much of this tortuous reasoning, we can suggest that the case for psychological disturbance is still not clear, and very few studies have actually matched their samples to the real population. They are either too old, too male-dominated, too professionally biased, include prelingually-deaf people, or are drawn from clinical referrals (thus increasing the likelihood of psychological problems). Having said that, it has to be acknowledged that it is difficult to work with this group. The weakest conclusion is probably the most tenable. People losing their hearing experience problems of adaptation and are likely to enter a phase where their behaviour is 'maladjusted' as compared to the general population. The extent to which this causes anxiety in the individual will determine the likelihood of later problems.

SOCIAL EFFECTS

Even now I find myself wondering from time to time who I really am. Hearing people often think I am hearing because my speech is good, deaf people often think I am hearing because my signs are bad. ... Hearing people have their culture based on spoken language and deaf people have their culture based on sign language and we are caught between incomprehensible speech on the one hand and incomprehensible signs on the other. (Eliot 1978, in Luey 1980)

Not surprisingly, it is difficult to separate the social and psychological effects of deafness. An early report on its effects was provided by Beethoven in 1802 in what has subsequently become known as the Heiligenstadt Document. Writing some sixteen years prior to becoming completely deaf, he felt, concerning his deafness, that:

Though endowed with a passionate and lively temperament and even fond of the distraction offered by society, I was soon obliged to seclude myself and live in solitude ... if I appear in company I am overcome by a burning anxiety, a fear that I am running the risk of letting people know my condition ... Such experiences have almost made me despair, and I was on the point of putting an end to my life – the only thing that held me back was my art. (Quotation from Beethoven, Heiligenstadt Document, 1802)

Even when a degree of social interaction is maintained, there often emerge strategies on the part of the hearing-impaired to cope with the difficulties of conversation. Harriet Martineau writing in 1877 described one such technique, that of monopolizing or dominating conversation in order to avoid the need to understand what others have said. Martineau wrote that:

One of the bad consequences of my deafness has been making me far too much of a talker, and though friends whom I can trust aver that I am also a good listener, I certainly have never allowed a fair share of time and opportunity to slower and more modest and considerate speakers. (vol. 2: 216)

The difficulty that people with an acquired hearing loss face is therefore twofold. There is their own psychological adjustment to the new situation in which they find themselves, and the reaction of others to their condition.

Social interaction can be dominated by a sense of stigma. Heider and Heider (1941) identified impatience with deaf people's slowness in understanding what was being said to them as creating a feeling that they were inferior. This led to either over-protection or misunderstanding. It was Levine's (1960) view that the often detected trauma that occurred following acquired hearing loss as opposed to the relatively contented outlook of those born deaf lay in the circumstances of their respective lifestyles. The prelingually deaf had, in most cases, developed in the company of their deaf associates; those with acquired deafness, however, had been an integral part of the hearing world. The isolation a person suffers, therefore, is seen as being imposed by impaired hearing. The difficulty experienced in adjusting voice volume to suit the constantly changing environmental conditions encountered leads to additional stress. 'They are constantly on the alert', wrote Levine (1960), 'to detect the unfavourable reaction of those with whom they talk', so that a situation often arises where trying to understand what is said is added to the burden of trying not to be misunderstood.

It is hardly surprising that from this dual tension a rift may develop with others in the community. A hearing person's prejudice, or inability to exercise sufficient flexibility to meet the new requirements of communication with a person with acquired hearing loss, can result in social isolation on the one hand and social dependence on the other. Should acquired deafness occur in an adult possessing a high degree of social maturity and autonomy, dependence can emerge as a problem as everyday acts such as relying on others to make telephone calls on one's behalf threatens or is perceived as a threat to autonomy.

Denmark (1969) recognized the emergence of an autonomy problem but added that man is essentially a social being and that the primary function of hearing in adults is to maintain a relationship with the total environment. By being unable to understand the conversation of those around them, a sense of no longer participating is created. This sort of situation is worsened by the social stereotype which develops: isolated means does not care, hearing-impaired means stubborn and self-centred and so on.

Nett (1960) found that the most common reaction to a situation in which they were unable to follow what was being said was to obtain assistance from others, pretending or guessing what was being said, or doing nothing. Markides et al. (1979) argued that there existed a tendency to withdraw from society, from social, leisure, and spiritual situations and activities. Breed, Van der Horst, and Mous (1980) found that loss of contact with former acquaintances is common, and that as a result of communication difficulties a fear of attempting to establish new contacts emerged. A feeling that even if they make such an attempt there may be rejection often leads to no attempt being made at all, therefore reinforcing the sense of isolation that exists. Kyle and Wood (1983) found 87 per cent said that hearing people did not understand the problems of deafness.

Breed, Van der Horst, and Mous (1980) in addition highlighted the effect on relations with one's children. It was found in the Netherlands study (published in Hamburg as conference proceedings) that a tendency emerged for them to increasingly turn to the parent with normal hearing. Although reactions varied, some children apparently found the situation so difficult to accept and cope with that they were even reluctant to go shopping with the deafened mother or father. Even when the children managed to cope, problems arose when they brought home school-friends, as often they had little experience or idea on how to cope. Breed, Van der Horst, and Mous concluded that this added an extra tension to a relationship already under a great deal of pressure following the onset of hearing loss.

Richtberg and Bochnik (1980) suggested hearing loss represented a break in the natural life-flow, characterized by the painful loss of many well-known experiences and achievements. The handicap led to a forced renunciation of many things previously taken for granted as well as developments and plans for the future. The outcome was viewed with total pessimism in that it meant one could no longer be what one once was, and that one could no longer become what one once hoped to become. Thomas (1984), too, reported reduction in friendship and interaction and that people gave up many of their social activities.

Beattie (1981) concentrated in her survey on the social aspects of acquired hearing loss in adults although only 25 per cent of her ninety-six participants with mild losses were under the age of 60. It was found that a strategy existed amongst the majority of drawing attention to their deafness only if conversational difficulties arose. Beattie found, however, that men were more likely to tell people that they had a hearing loss than women, but that on the other hand employed men were less likely to tell than either retired men or employed women. A majority of those interviewed considered that other people were found to be helpful when aware of their deafness. Two-thirds could think of communication situations which had resulted in embarrassment and frustration. Kyle and Wood (1983) report similar results with never more than 20 per cent prepared to divulge the secret of their hearing loss in public. Loneliness, often considered to be an outcome of hearing loss, was reported by a quarter of Beattie's sample with men experiencing this more often than women. Even when this did not occur, a majority considered that the quality of their social life had been adversely affected, 60 per cent of the sample rating difficulty in dealing with group conversation as the most important.

Bunting's (1981) survey of the public's attitude towards the deaf supported the stereotype described by Hunt (1944), i.e. that of possessing a fear of new situations, ridicule, and chance encounters, and likely to try to hide their deafness from others. Kyle and Wood (1983) focused on the impact of acquired hearing loss personally, socially, and vocationally. Interviews were conducted with 105 subjects resident in the county of Avon, aged between 25 and 55, with an overall average of ten years' recency of onset. Some 88 per cent of subjects 'agreed' or 'strongly agreed' with the statement that deaf people experienced greater loneliness than hearing people, with the same number considering that people with a hearing loss are often frustrated in expressing themselves. Regarding social life, 74 per cent felt that a person who became deaf could not continue with the same social life as before. It was shown how the problem of communication emerged even when the degree of hearing loss was mild except in close proximity to others such as at mealtimes. The sample interviewed did feel that disadvantages were associated with deafness, such as an increase in irritability as a result of dealing with others. It was interesting to note that the views expressed are similar to the findings of Bunting (1981) when she asked hearing people about their image of the effects of deafness. Also of significance from a societal viewpoint was that no effect was found to exist regarding age or recency of onset on these attitudes. Again, because of the same sampling problems and the lack of adequate control groups, it is very difficult to establish the accuracy of what seems to be a consistent stereotype: isolation, withdrawal, re-evaluation of social life. When we later discuss data on families it should be possible to extend the analysis further and establish how useful such general findings are.

VOCATIONAL EFFECTS

Thus, an electronic technician who wore no aid mistook instructions and was labelled stupid and inattentive; she 'took to writing down all instructions and met with much impatience and annoyance'; after additional mistakes she was fired. The owner of a large farm machinery business had a nervous breakdown trying to operate it with a severe hearing loss. ... A financial administrator whose work required much group conversation 'was scared to death that I would ultimately make a very serious, costly error'; a nurse worried about not hearing the alarm in a critical care unit. (Orlans and Meadow-Orlans 1985)

Needless to say, the problems of sampling are particularly acute when it comes to examining employment prospects. The principal studies shed some light on this area, but none of them have completely satisfactory samples to determine employment effects. However, various results have been reported. Levine (1960) referred to the reluctance of employers and the presence of misconceptions concerning the implications of disability. Phillips (1973) attempted by way of a survey in the USA to identify the main reasons for this negative attitude, and found that employers gave these as (a) safety risks, (b) the deaf are inflexible, (c) the deaf are difficult to train.

In a study carried out in France by Cottin (1973) on the consequences for employment subsequent to a hearing loss occurring, it was found that 50 per cent of the sample had to change their occupation. Thomas (1984) had a different result:

The onset of hearing loss does not result in an increased likelihood of unemployment. Nor apparently, is it associated with 'underemployment', that is, being forced into a job with diminished status, or lessened promotion prospects. It also seems that hearing-impaired people do not see themselves as being forced to change jobs in the future. (89)

Pointing out that these findings were similar to those of Hyde, Pattison, and Sherman (1981), whose study had been carried out in Australia, he reiterated the view that they were in contrast to the official statement of the British Society of Audiology (Markides *et al.* 1979) which identified the emergence of a range of severe vocational limitations that included a difficulty in maintaining employment, promotional limitations, changing employment, and underemployment. Factors which did emerge, however, were a proneness among the hearing-impaired to worry about their work, and being less happy at work than their hearing counterparts. When those possessing a severe hearing impairment were examined as a sub-sample, there was still found to be no evidence of direct unemployment.

Kyle and Wood (1985) found that there was no significant change in job status as a result of hearing loss although the slight movement that existed did seem to be downward. This was the case even when 73 per cent said the communication aspect of their job was important or absolutely essential. Ninety-five per cent of subjects felt that they could continue with their job but only a minority of 39 per cent had actually informed their employer about their hearing loss. In the end, it was found that 96 per cent of subjects had actually retained the same job before and after the onset of hearing loss.

In dealing with interaction at work most people used their hearing aid alone (93 per cent as against 6 per cent who used lip-reading). Communication difficulties still arose, however, in that 16 per cent said that they 'often' did not fully understand instructions with a further 65 per cent saying that this happened 'sometimes'. Little problem emerged in their relations with workmates, with 92 per cent feeling that they were talked to just as often as before their deafness and 72 per cent feeling that they were always included in conversations. Reduced promotion prospects were considered to exist and with it the attitude that it would be very difficult for a deaf person to get a job.

In contrast there was found to exist a strong positive attitude towards employment itself. A measure of job satisfaction and well-being set out by Warr, Cook, and Wall (1979) was adapted. This measure had been standardized on hearing groups primarily in factory and engineering settings. The measurement of job satisfaction produced an interesting pattern and one which essentially confirmed the findings of Trevains (1982) who had observed that deafened people are likely to be happier in their jobs than other workers. It was significant, however, that despite their job satisfaction being at a high level, the subjects did not consider that their jobs contained the characteristics which would normally accompany such a level of job satisfaction. There was evidence, therefore, that deaf people could be considered 'underemployed' in relation to their positive attitude towards their job.

Jobs therefore do not pose the major threat they were thought to have done. People do not lose their jobs simply because of hearing loss but the nature of the job and the personal adjustment could make the job less secure and increase the likelihood of lack of promotion. In effect, the hearing loss affects the quality of employment life and lays the individual open to a whole series of anxiety-provoking situations. Cooke's (1984) personal account and Cox's (1985) views are particularly appropriate in showing the fragility of the personal contact at work:

> At the start of my last term I had to attend a lunchtime meeting of lecturers and students during which the head of the department addressed a few words specifically to me. Standing there, uncomprehending across the room, I could only guess at what he was saying. The students all looked at me and I saw they knew that I was deaf. (Cooke 1984: 36)

People with a hearing loss may have to face this anxiety daily and therefore value jobs where their abilities 'to guess' are not constantly tested.

THE RESULTS OF HEARING LOSS

We can see that hearing loss is not a simple, easily described condition. It has evoked stereotypes and problems since it has been first reported. It strikes at the heart of human life – communication. Degree of loss, phase of life when onset occurs, factors in the social, work, and psychological environments, all contribute to the individual's attempts to cope. We can discount psychotic reactions, particularly paranoid ones, and job loss as certain outcomes. Nevertheless, we can begin to see the level of strain which the individual must experience in order to survive. The chapters which follow and the results we report attempt to explore this further. The aim is to understand the onset, development, and outcomes of hearing loss in a way which will allow us to act to decrease the stress on the individual and those around.

3

Relationships, disability, and illness behaviour: relevant theories

It is not surprising to find that when we come to consider hearing-impairment in the context of home life we multiply our problems in understanding coping strategies. There is a complex set of relationships and the interaction both influences and is influenced by coping with the hearing impairment. Yet it is certain that people at home are a major force in the coping. The individual differences in hearing-impaired people will be reflected in their relationships. The degree of supportiveness, understanding, and coping will produce the final strategies of adjustment. There has been very little research work on hearing impairment in families and we will discuss this later. However, it is important first to try to understand what the family is and how theorists and researchers have come to describe it.

We use the term 'family' to mean people living together 'at home'. It could be a pattern similar to the traditional one of husband, wife, and children or any unit where people choose to live together. The nuclear family is undergoing change in our society and the growing number of one-parent families testifies to the changing statistics of 'family life'. The ideal picture of these 'family' relations is of supportive interaction, caring, and help. One would expect them to be constantly moving towards stress-free resolutions to problems rather than to conflict and confrontation. Families ought to 'understand' when a member gets into difficulty. The resolution of the problems takes many forms and the type of communication adopted makes it extremely difficult to consider an 'ideal' structure.

The study of the 'family' has become increasingly important over the last forty years. One way of looking at families is to use the 'systems' model of family interaction (e.g. Haley and Hoffman 1967, and Jackson 1974). Family therapy based on these theories uses Jackson's concept of 'homeostasis', a balance which is arrived at within a family. The presence of disablement or handicap disturbs this balance and the way the family changes and restructures itself becomes the central area of concern. The important recent changes brought about by family therapy are part of the move away from the psychoanalytic practice of individual therapy and of treating people in isolation and a move towards understanding people in a context of other relationships. The psychodynamic view of the individual psyche has been constantly changing but psychiatrists such as Bion (1960) with his studies of soldiers after the Second World War moved the emphasis away from the individual completely. The need to look at individuals in the context of a group arose because of soldiers' interaction and common experience of war. This emphasis on group work gathered strength in the 1950s and 1960s, focusing on people in a 'system'. This in turn was extended by the growth of 'family therapy'. Poster (1978), in his theoretical view of the family, saw the individual set in the context of relationships. It is within this framework that we also wish to examine the way adults adjust to acquired hearing loss.

The importance of communication in the family (Bateson *et al.* 1956) and of messages and signals, meaningful only within relationships, is of particular relevance where the communication is severely threatened by the loss of hearing. Reuch and Bateson's theory of the double-bind in conversation – saying one thing but giving clear messages of another meaning – is particularly relevant to 'spoiled communication'. That is, where stress occurs or where there are disturbances in family interaction psychologically or auditorily the meaning of messages becomes blurred. When this occurs family functioning is threatened and the solution is provided either by clarifying the meaning or by mediation by other family members. It is not possible here to go much more deeply into the study of families since it is a huge area, but we will draw on further ideas in relation to the problems arising in the face of disability.

FAMILIES WITH CHILDREN WHO ARE ILL OR DISABLED

We can move on now from wider theories of the family and disability to specific work on families with children who are disabled or ill.

All families cope with disasters differently, there are the 'solids' who have resources enough in themselves to cope and who can fall back on other members of the family whose relationships are lasting and cannot be disturbed, and there are the 'brittles' who are shattered and helpless and need much support from outside agencies. Probably we all fall between these two extremes. (Hannam 1975: 67)

This is a view expressed about families with children with mental handicap, by the father of a son with a mental handicap. Dividing families up into types is common. Minuchin (1974) describes families with rigid boundaries as disengaged and with diffuse boundaries as enmeshed between sub-systems within the family, i.e. mother and child. This description of 'normal' families implies ways of adapting to stress of the kind produced by hearing loss. 'A family adapts to stress in a way that maintains family continuity while making restructuring possible. If a family responds to stress with rigidity, dysfunctional patterns occur' (Minuchin 1974: 43).

The trend in the UK is for the parents to be made central in any dealings with their children rather than seeing the family as a whole. The Warnock report (1978) and the Education Act (1981) make it essential that parents are consulted at every stage of the process of referral, assessment, and treatment. However, Tomlinson (1982) shows how this theory breaks down in the face of class divisions with vocal, secure families more able to direct their problems outwards and in effect secure greater help from services.

As for the families themselves, Thomas (1978) provides a useful review of their coping with handicapped children. Some parents have been reported as suffering shock, refusal, bitterness, envy, rejection, yet by different analysis one might claim that these parents are normal. Their 'maladjustment' is part of the process of change. What is clear is that discovery of handicap is stressful and requires the family to come to terms not only with the child and their own competence but also with the interference and scrutiny of outside agencies, concerned for the welfare of the child. Responses to this situation range from overprotection and denial to a search for perfection in the child through unrealistic expectations. In addition, the family may have to cope with the 'courtesy stigma'. This means that by association, they become part of the disabled world – by sharing in the stigma applied to their disabled family member they too may be stigmatized by others (Birenbaum 1970). However, the lack of clear-cut results in these studies indicates the degree of complexity of family interaction. To take as a basic principle that there is an interaction between family and handicap means one can measure the effects. Previous work has concentrated on families with children with chronic illness or handi-cap. Kew (1975) writes:

> Until the parents themselves begin to see the handicap as a truly family event and not just in terms of the *special needs* of their handicapped child, then stability and equilibrium are bound to remain upset in some other perhaps unnoticed area of family life. (21)

Using this family-centred approach he argues that family functioning is disrupted by the impact of a handicapped child. There are changes in:

1 the parental distribution of affection and support amongst children in the family;
2 the allocation of domestic responsibility;
3 the allocation of blame for family disasters;
4 the relationship between husband and wife.

This redistribution of time and attention by the parents directly affects siblings more than the mere 'presence' of a handicapped child. This may constitute a major upheaval in the family way of life in the search for the right coping strategies.

This process is influenced by another important element. Where comparison was possible with 'normal' landmarks (speaking, crawling, walking) in a child's development, then this made adjustment easier for parents (Hewett 1970). This may have implications for adults' life patterns in relation to disability if age-specific norms exist; if career promotion, relationships, marriage, or birth of children take place at the expected time, adjustment may perhaps more easily occur. Failing to fulfil these expectations (which in times of unemployment and changing relationship structures may not be nearly so rigid anyway) does presumably diminish the normality of the life one is leading. However, estimation of what are expected 'norms' in adult life are far less clear cut than those for child development. The problem with this is that 'normal' behaviour may become a burden. Hartmann (1985) comments that children who are deaf have to be more normal than normal, i.e. they are not allowed to be naughty but have to be passive, good, and conforming and are not encouraged to be adventurous.

An alternative approach has been to examine the process or stages with which the family must cope. Davis (1963), studying the effect of polio on families, suggested four stages:

39

1 prelude stage – awareness that something is wrong and that it is probably serious;
2 warning stage – realization of this diagnosis;
3 impact stage – diagnosis;
4 inventory or adjustment stage.

This is a summarized version of the phases of stress-events in a study of mass disasters (Powell and Rayne 1952).

Harrison (1975) looked at families with children with cystic fibrosis or Perthes Disease, using the 'situational' approach. This involves 'events' in the illness-situation 'with a view to suggesting the type and timing of intervention to alleviate stress arising from those events which are influenceable by policy' (9). She summarizes illness-situations in this way:

1 All illness-situations are composed of static or *structural* elements (incidence, demographic factors, symptoms, etc.) which are *outside the control* of individuals, and *dynamic* elements (patient career) and stress or crisis-provoking events occurring during the patient career. The latter are associated with the nature of the condition and the need for treatment, factors of communication, finance and occupation and supportive services and reference group activity.

2 The greater a) the amount of functional information conveyed about an illness; b) the amount of information conveyed about the management of an illness; c) the financial resources available; d) the provision of supportive services; e) the functional support of reference group interaction – the less the experienced stress. (155)

Harrison isolates four main stress-provoking factors in her research: communication, finance and occupation, absence of supportive services, and stress itself. The first three are influenced by social policy. Her conclusions imply policy changes in professional education on communication with patients, and information-sharing between departments, and further research on the *timing* of intervention. Others have also highlighted part of Harrison's second factor – finance. There are obvious practical factors directly related to finance. Baldwin (1984) has looked at the differential costs of caring for a handicapped child in order to demonstrate how fundamentally this affects the family's experience of handicap. Her conclusions are that disability produces financial hardship and at times real poverty.

One can see the unique difficulties that parents of a disabled child have to face, yet the traumatic rearrangement of family life is also common to those families where adults acquire a disability. In this case we might expect additional problems.

FAMILIES WITH ADULT DISABILITY

Scott (1969) has shown how blindness produces a change in self-image because of the altered perception by others. The work by Lewis *et al.* (1976) emphasized the lack of one consistent pattern of coping response. In order to analyse coping strategies within the family one is required to see the family as a changing dynamic group anyway in contrast to the linear approach which concentrates on the individual patient. The more 'dynamic' approach emphasizes the interaction and consequently 'distributes responsibility for dysfunction throughout the family system', as Shapiro (1983) puts it. Using a family approach to disability means assuming that the way in which the members behave towards each other influences the coping process, and that changing that behaviour alters the individual's response to disability. It does mean that to take this approach involves a more complex view not only of the family but also of its interaction with people in the external environment, e.g. health professionals.

ILLNESS BEHAVIOUR

The qualitative data will be presented in Chapters 9 and 10. The method used relies on the work on illness behaviour. The case for hearing loss being considered in the context of illness behaviour has a number of strong arguments. Lay theories of what 'deafness' or hearing loss is will be part of this behaviour. Beliefs about what happens when your hearing declines will obviously be dependent on localized 'patient' cultures but will also be the outcome of interaction (if there is any) with health workers in the field as well as with friends and relatives. This is particularly relevant in hearing loss where there is often a familial disposition. The response of and towards other members of the family is particularly important. The study uses Dingwall's 1976 analysis of illness action as a basis for exploring this area. He has stressed the importance of commonsense reasoning about 'illness' to understand the meaningful world of the patient. We are forced to consider his or her own social circumstances which have particular relevance here in shaping responses to a change in stable 'illness behaviour'. This model has something to offer in the case of a response to a diagnosis of a hearing loss – informants are in many cases left to make sense of their own position, sometimes with very little information. There are comparisons to be made here with West's (1979) work on children with epilepsy and Voysey's (1975) work on parents of children who are disabled. West (1979) writes:

> Lay knowledge is the means by which parents usually assess what it is their children has and whether or not to contact the doctor, and in the continual process of making sense of their problem it is always a major point of reference.

Making sense of the diagnosis is very important in this situation. Acceptance of the label of 'hard-of-hearing' or 'deaf' (once it is given) is part of this process which can be interpreted as being very much linked to illness behaviour. There are interesting similarities here with the Lindow (1986) work on 'The social consequences of seeing a psychiatrist'. There a group of twenty people were interviewed having been referred to a psychiatrist and were seen before and after the consultation. Another twenty-two long-term psychiatric patients were interviewed with particular emphasis in both groups on 'felt stigma'. The similarities occur in the process of seeking help, making sense of the diagnosis if given, and the effects of the label once given. Lindow writes:

> Those who consult a psychiatrist for the first time are drawn from the general public and hold the same range of attitudes and stereotypes about mental illness. They will include among them both the 'wise' (Goffman's (1963) term for sympathisers with a stigmatised group) and the prejudiced. It seems highly likely that a high proportion of those who either refuse psychiatric referral by their GPs or fail to attend their first appointment hold a strong negative stereotype. (79–80)

This quote could just as easily be used to describe audiology departments or ear, nose and throat clinics where the population we are concerned with are often accused of non-attendance or non-compliance (in the sense of not wearing a hearing aid). The attitudes expressed by our informants towards hearing loss in general and other people who have a hearing loss certainly can be viewed in the category of the 'wise' and the 'prejudiced'. People's knowledge of hearing loss is likely to vary. This illustration of how important people's beliefs are in theories of illness are relevant to looking at the 'moral career' of becoming hard-of-hearing. An excellent summary of Goffman's work on stigma-management strategies is given by Lindow and is useful for our purposes:

1 denial (that the labelled behaviour took place);
2 exceptionalization (behaviour not an example of the stigma);
3 excusing (some other reason for behaviour);
4 normalization (deviant label invalid, behaviour normal);
5 identity politics (changed perceptions of label);
6 deviance disavowal (stress unstigmatized aspects of self).

These categories are valuable for looking at how hearing impairment is perceived. Hearing loss will be placed firmly in the context of illness behaviour and Goffman's work on stigma. Although there is no desire for hearing loss to be seen in a medical context, illness behaviour offers insight into how to analyse the response to hearing loss. The collective qualitative data is well discussed in Kirk and Miller (1986) where the validity of this method is demonstrated.

HEARING LOSS AND RELATIONSHIPS

There have been some attempts to consider hearing loss within relationships. Thomas, Lamont, and Harris (1982) report from their first study that 'although hearing loss was associated with psychological disturbance, there was no obvious adverse effect on family life' (132). In the sense that the proportion of separated or divorced people were the same as in the general population, people were not more likely to have arguments or spend less time with their families. In their second study the proportion of the sample who were divorced or separated was very high – this was amongst people with a severe sensori-neural hearing loss. Those who participated in the family study were felt to be relatively well-adjusted, as they self-selected into this section of the study (and the refusal rate was high).

Among the conclusions were:

1 There is considerable evidence of stress both for the respondent and the normally hearing members of the family.
2 Much of the stress experienced by the respondents appears to have been alleviated by their supportive families. Giving such

support could be a source of stress for the normally hearing members of the family.

3 Environmental aids could play an important part in improving the quality of life of the whole family.

4 Family counselling initiated at the first hearing-aid issue is strongly recommended.

The first study (Thomas and Herbst 1980) showed that many respondents felt members of their families did not really understand what it meant to lose one's hearing. Hyde, Pattison and Sherman (1981) found that 50 per cent of their sample of 390 people wanted trained counselling for their families although, interestingly, 81 per cent of the tinnitus sufferers felt that it would be inappropriate. Thomas (1984) recommended taking counselling into both the home and workplace.

Breed, Van der Horst, and Mous (1980) found that hearing children tended to go to the hearing parent more than to the hearing-impaired parent. Beattie (1981) found teenagers and daughters of all ages emerged as particularly difficult (partly this was felt as daughters were more likely to be the ones looking after elderly hard-of-hearing parents and therefore more directly in line for complaints about in-sensitivity!). Beattie also found evidence of 'protectors' or 'benefactors' within the family. A similar concept was used by Von der Leith (1972a) in the 'relay-station' – relationships where one person transmitted messages from the rest of the family. Beattie had found that any hard-of-hearing adult living with *two or more hearing people* was more likely to experience isolation than living with only one because of the external conversations.

We can see again that there is no clear-cut finding on the effects of acquired disability except to say that it is complex and varying. There is still one piece in the jigsaw which has not been examined and that is the position and experience of those partners most closely associated with the disabled person.

THE CARERS

Pauline Ashley (1985), writing of her husband Jack Ashley's sudden hearing loss, quotes David Wright, a poet, who is deaf, saying that 'it is the non-deaf who absorb a large part of the impact of disability'. He calls it the 'converse aspects of deafness – the other half of the dialogue'. The other half of the dialogue is something of which very little is written. Although Pauline Ashley does not agree entirely with Wright's conviction of the extent of the hearing person's absorption of the impact of deafness, she acknowledges there is a very real impact on the hearing people in the relationship. Understanding the other side of communication is vital to understanding hearing loss.

A very new area in social policy which is relevant is the study of 'caring' in relationships (e.g. Finch and Groves 1983, Briggs and Oliver 1985, EOC 1981, 1982). 'Caring demands both love and labour' (Graham 1983) and the interest is in the change in relationships of the person being 'looked after' and the other 'taking care'. The partner has a role in 'looking out for' the other person's needs, anticipating them, and altering behaviour to accommodate those needs. The existence of 'protectors' or 'benefactors' in families is an example of this (Beattie 1981). Attempts to 'care for the carers' are being made because caring within the family is now seen as a valuable resource and one which saves residential care.

Shearer (1981) quotes Hunt (1966) talking about the 'Aren't they wonderful' school of thought about disability: 'The unfortunate person is assumed to have wonderful and exceptional courage. This devalues other people by implication and leaves the fit person still with his original view that the disablement is really something utterly tragic' (24). Shearer then goes on to apply this to the other person in the relationship:

> this is as true if the person singled out for praise is the person who lives with someone with a disability if their mothers, wives or husbands are 'wonderful' for coping, where does that leave the people who have the disability? It leaves them with a problem. (108)

This attitude towards the hearing partner needs to be avoided – it is not helpful to either party and patronizing to both. A much more constructive approach is Ferguson and Watts' (1980) 'prime agents of change' where the hearing person is seen as having a valuable contribution to make. Caring involves finding out the needs of *both* partners and providing support if necessary. 'Recognition and help' were the two things asked for by the 'caring wives' Oliver (1983) talked to. The Association of Carers was set up in 1981 as a self-help group for people caring at home recognizing that they had their own needs.

Caring then is an occupation all of its own. It requires all of the virtues we normally assign to it – patience, competence, helpfulness – but most of all it requires recognition. The other side of caring is dependency and the consumer's view of disablement is one increasingly being taken into account. (Campling 1981, Ashley 1985). The 'expert' view by the 'insider' is at last being taken seriously. The refusal to accept the 'ideological cripple' label (Abberley 1985) means not accepting the 'mourning' or 'grieving' model of disability (Dickinson 1977, Weller and Miller 1977).

IMPLICATIONS

The literature on relationships, disability, and illness behaviour has valuable insights for interpreting the data in the present study. How people cope with a hearing loss acquired in adult life, particularly in terms of their closest relationships, varies tremendously according to their situation before the loss. What the literature offers is a way of interpreting these coping strategies. Firstly by offering ways of analysing relationships, secondly by providing ways of looking at the effects of an acquired disability, and thirdly by providing a way of collecting information about the effects of the disability by trying to use the perceptions of the person who has experienced that loss.

4

Understanding adjustment

Here one must make a particular plea to the very young who seem to me to speak with less and less clarity and less and less precision of articulation than perhaps we did in the past. My own grandchildren frequently tell me their grandpa is getting deaf. I say, 'No, it is just that you all mumble.' They do mumble and I hope that the schools will do something to improve the articulation of our children. If they do that they will certainly improve the lives of those children's grandparents. (Winstanley 1983: 1154)

As one progresses through life, events have to be interpreted and reinterpreted. Most people would expect to look for consistencies in their own view of their world. People feel that change occurs externally rather than internally. Only when faced with obvious and irreversible change does the individual have to 'adjust'.

To get to this point, we have perhaps come a long way round in the first chapters through an exploration of disability, hearing loss, and the family. This background is almost essential, we believe, to obtain any real understanding of the task the individual faces. The problem is that the task can be defined differently according to age, situation, and other life-factors like the change occurring in the above quotation. Depending on whether you are deaf, or are receiving 'treatment' as deaf, or are providing that treatment, a different set of descriptions appear. What has been lacking in the field of hearing loss is any sort of 'whole-world' view as distinct from views from these stances. Two concepts, we feel, offer the tools to understand the situation: *adjustment* and *control*. The former is the description of the task and its dynamics: how does the individual change over time and in response to events? The latter is the explanation of the force for change in the individual. We propose that the individual establishes a position, a functional way of life, which varies according to different aspects or situations in life, which becomes the expectation of the individual in relation to the environment. It indicates the extent to which the individual influences and/or is influenced by the environment and the characters which populate it. Hearing loss affects this position and adjustment is the process whereby attempts are made to maintain the level of control or to negotiate a new level.

In many respects, as we will now discuss, this is not a fundamentally new view in the study of people but it has not been used to any marked extent to understand hearing loss. The most popular view is typified by the rehabilitation model. This is in essence a 'medical model' though it is not confined to medical professionals. Indeed, it is just as likely to be the basis of educational provision, where it is termed remediation. Alpiner (1980) explains this model of aural rehabilitation extremely clearly and shows how assessment of the individual's objective performance audiologically and communicatively is made the basis of a programme of remediation or therapy. Although Alpiner's model is thorough and includes recourse to family discussion and real-world intervention, e.g. at work, it essentially rests on a fundamental of the medical view that the individual should recognize the extent of the problem. However, at the same time the problem can only be fully specified by the independent professional. This is very much the view expressed to Hegarty and Pocklington (1983) concerning what hearing therapists' roles ought to be in the UK. Their evaluation of the success of hearing therapy training rests on the premise that they are to be trained to do this very job of helping the individual to come to terms with the problem as defined by the professional. Safilios-Rothschild (1981) voices an increasingly powerful dissident view of this process of 'marginalization':

> Those who become disabled when they are teenagers or adults have experienced at least for some years the majority status of non-disabled persons. They have been socialized into the majority status of an able-bodied person and into the prejudiced attitudes towards the disabled. Since the success of rehabilitation has been equated with the 'acceptance of disability', that is, with the relinquishing of majority status rights, rehabilitation entails a highly stressful resocialization process into an 'inferior' status. (7)

People acquiring disability have begun to question the whole principle of the need for personal insight into the condition, especially when that insight has to be defined in terms of external professionals or others. Glass (1985), in an interesting aside, tells of annotating a paper on people's attitudes towards their family and hearing loss with the comment 'the authors should have interviewed the family members' because of their potential insights, while a deaf friend disagreed as if to say that no one could fully understand in the way that the hearing-impaired person could. The views of others may be interesting but they do not represent reality for the hearing-impaired person. Oliver (1981) uses Mead's (1934) symbolic interactionism, which sees the importance not in the events but in the meaning attached to them by participants, as a way of explaining the difficulties arising in disability.

To cope with hearing loss some negotiation is required not at the physical, real-world event level but rather at the level of meaning assigned by participants. That is to say, hearing loss is viewed differently by different people and its effects are thereby different. At home, at work, in society, hearing-impaired people meet others and will have to negotiate each time. This negotiation determines how much of a handicap it will become. At different times in life very different environmental forces and considerations will impinge on the individual.

PHASES AND STATES

To build a meaningful picture of the change occurring in hearing loss, we need to consider two parallel developmental patterns. The first we wish to suggest is the phase through which the individual is passing and the second is the life-state in which the individual is placed.

Figure 4.1   Phases in hearing loss over time

Phase 1	Phase 2	Phase 3	Phase 4
	1	1	1
	X	Y	Z
Birth	Onset	Diagnosis	Hearing aid/ rehabilitation

Kyle, Jones, and Wood (1985) have in a tentative model offered three phases of hearing loss. For our purposes we wish to add a fourth, or rather a first: the stage prior to hearing loss onset. We can schematize the phases and states as in Figures 4.1 and 4.2.

Phase 1 is what Safilios Rothschild (1981) calls the period of normal socialization. In effect, people's early lives will be characterized by a whole series of important and different influences which will construct the person who reaches time X. This is a key position which Meadow-Orlans (1985) wants to be 'age at onset' since it is vital to determining the effects of hearing loss. Unfortunately, in our studies (Kyle and Wood 1983 and Kyle, Wood, and Jones 1983) and as is also pointed out by Thomas (1984), X is not a point, at least not a point *in time* for the majority of people. Hearing loss is gradual for most people and the beginning of hearing loss is not determinable. Personal recollections and retrospective interviewing only emphasize the frustration of trying to determine actual onset. Age at which it was first noticed is not acceptable to our model since we propose that adjustment has already begun by this time. We have therefore only a conceptual point of onset at X but in reality a shift (albeit gradual) from phase 1, socialization, to phase 2, hearing loss.

Phase 2 is characterized by coping behaviour. We predict individuals will transfer their hearing problems to faults in others or in the environment. Rather like Winstanley at the beginning of this section, 'other people mumble', telephone lines are bad, pubs and restaurants are too noisy, people look away when talking. Cox (1985) describes a whole list of strategies which emerge almost unconsciously.

> I notice I now sit at the front of the lecture theatres .... I found I usually place myself at the end of a row on a table to avoid having to turn my head to the wall to speak to a left side neighbour .... In meetings I prefer to sit opposite someone who is likely to do most of the talking .... In conversation I can only be absolutely certain of what is said if I have said it which means that to participate I am inclined to want to speak and thus dominate the conversation .... I find it hard to laugh when I haven't seen the joke and am aware that this makes me seem humourless. (9)

In her case, Cox is in a later phase but this is behaviour we would also predict in phase 2. It is supported repeatedly in the personal stories of hearing loss.

Kyle, Jones, and Wood (1985) have set out a picture of the movement

from mild loss towards recognition of a loss (Figure 4.2). In this
the individual begins to break social norms for loudness (or more
accurately signal-to-noise ratios). That is, the loss makes people speak
too loudly in quiet places, and too quietly in noisy places, makes them
likely to alter television volume, sit closer to speakers, strain to hear,
ask for repetitions, and so on. In fact, what is happening is that the
individual tries to maintain the personal level of sound, but in doing so
alters the sound levels for those around. In doing so, social norms may
be broken and the individual has to accept lower levels or face ostracism.
The frequency of the breaching of social norms is likely to increase as
the person comes to a realization and acceptance that something is
wrong. At that point they move into phase 3.

**Figure 4.2   Phase 1: increasingly regular testing of socially
acceptable loudness levels**

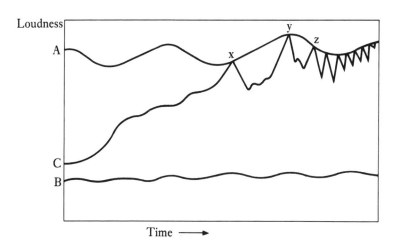

Phase 3 is the period of uncertainty, a time when most change and
adaptation is held in abeyance. 'Waiting for the verdict' is the most
likely situation. The hearing-impaired person goes to the doctor on
one or more occasion to try to establish the degree of problem; in most
cases, referral to an audiology department will be swift and surgery and
audiological treatment will follow. In the majority of cases the issue of

a hearing aid is a likely final point of phase 3. During this time, people see the professionals as a solution: the medical view of treatment and cure is most appropriate. People await the verdict of the professionals and hope for a solution. Most of the health provision in the UK is concentrated in this period which for the majority of people will be only a few months.

In phase 4 the individual reaches the open-ended phase of coping, of living with hearing loss, of gradually becoming aware of the fact that life and position are changing. Without appearing too dramatic or alarmist, the speed with which these issues are encountered will be a function of the extent of hearing loss. Ashley (1985) describes it very negatively: 'The plunge from a normally hearing world into one of almost total silence meant the plummeting of my happiness, aspirations and hopes for the future.' (60) His deafness is 'total'. In milder hearing loss these effects will not be as extreme.

Phase 4 and phase 3 may be repeated. That is, an individual receives a hearing aid and begins to adapt. At a later point, a review of the case or a further deterioration in hearing may prompt surgery or re-examination (a return to phase 3). This will again be followed by a return to phase 4. Entry to phase 4 may be at the same hearing-loss level (e.g. provision of a more powerful hearing aid) or may be at a more serious loss (e.g. operation, accident, or deterioration producing profound loss). It is phase 4 which virtually all research has examined. All of the studies described in Chapter 2 deal with this period and usually, and significantly, from periods at a year beyond point 2 (diagnosis) in our figure (Figure 4.1). That is, people are not contacted immediately their hearing loss is diagnosed, are not even dealt with in the days after hearing aids are provided. Our research, in contrast, has asked; 'Are people with a hearing loss different according to whether or not they have *acknowledged* such a loss?' The emphasis is rightly on 'acknowledged' since if we believe the findings of Davis (1983) three-quarters of those with hearing losses are not in posession of a hearing aid. That is, normative data will include responses from members of the 'public' who are deaf themselves with which comparison is being made. Additionally, this fact implies that *three-quarters* of those with hearing loss are in phase 2 and *not* in phase 4 where research has been concentrated. It is therefore vital that we give attention to each phase of the lifespan of hearing loss. In addition, we wish to propose that the phases of hearing losses are influenced by the life-state of the individual. For the moment, we wish to propose only three aspects and these are not wholly independent. Later, we will need to review the extent of the life-state and the variables which seem to be most related to adjustment.

Figure 4.3   Individual life-states (three aspects) - one pattern

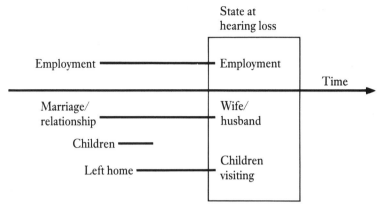

In suggesting life-state as a way of understanding hearing loss, we are only attempting to describe adequately the common claim in personal accounts that hearing loss affects different people in different ways. This seems rather obvious and also, in a way, discouraging. Unless we can identify the factors which are relevant at different phases then we are lost when it comes to adequate counselling. The life-state of the individual in the early stages of hearing loss is obviously critical in determining the response to the loss. Those in employment may be badly affected if their job involves buying and selling by telephone, or involves management of groups of people. At the same time, the problems at work may be alleviated by ease of communication at home by a particularly helpful family with no adolescent problems. These factors will be given or fixed during phase 2 but are more likely to be alterable by phase 4. In the study we will report in the next section, we attempt to identify the factors which contribute to the life-state of the individual. Our aim is to look for some simplicity in a very complex situation.

ADJUSTMENT

However, the main purpose in this chapter is to tackle the general question, 'what is adjustment?' That is, how can we consider the person who acquires a hearing loss and begins to change his life? What is positive change? What is good adjustment? How is coping understood? Is it possible for people not to adjust? Surprisingly, none of the answers to these questions are readily available. The majority of people do not die of deafness and are therefore faced with change, but we do not know how the change occurs, whether it is 'neurotic' in the sense Thomas (1984) concludes, nor whether we can influence it.

Various authors have recently tackled the area and it is worth trying to create a framework for our investigation. The word 'adjustment' is not particularly widely used. It tends not to appear in the index of books on hearing loss, e.g. Thomas (1984) or Schow and Nerbonne (1980). Perhaps we should say at the outset that we view adjustment as change in behaviour, belief, relations, or interaction occurring in the period from the onset of hearing loss whenever that actually is. This change may be conscious or it may not; it may be dependent on change in others or in the environment and, most fundamental of all, the change may lead to different behaviour in different circumstances by the same person.

We have already thought of this change in terms of control (Kyle, Jones, and Wood, 1985) but this is a holding concept for the present. Other writers have given it different names. Schlesinger (1985) sees the central dimension in behaviour as that of power and powerlessness. She traces a long line of research from Seligman's (1975) views on learned helplessness whereby with age people may, in western societies, develop an illusion of incompetence. For Schlesinger, power is not 'an intent to constrain other people, but a sensed ability to influence and control the environment' (103). Developed largely as a concept to understand disadvantaged groups in society, it is a condition into which one is socialized rather than one which the person develops. 'Powerlessness signifies an individual's self-perception as not having the cognitive competence, psychological skills, instrumental resources and support systems needed to influence his or her environment successfully' (Schlesinger 1985: 105). Deafness can produce just this powerlessness. The aural rehabilitation model as portrayed by Alpiner (1980) tends to emphasize the need for insight on the part of the hearing-impaired into the extent of their problem, i.e. rehabilitation requires the collusion of the impaired in their powerlessness.

Langer (1983) conceptualizes the problem as one of control. Again tracing a line of descent from Seligman, the 'psychology of control is about the control of oneself and one's perceptions of reality' (13). She sees the whole concept as fundamental to an understanding of the person.

54

Research has shown that the consequences of the belief in control are primarily positive regardless of whether or not the perception is either true or acted upon . . . . Indeed, perceiving control apparently is crucial not only to one's psychological well-being but to one's physical health as well. (13)

In effect, control derives from perceived choice. Deafness diminishes extent of choice (as do other disabilities) and deafness therefore threatens control.

Whether one uses power or control as the central concept, it explains only the need or the drive. We must ask what happens when this need cannot be fulfilled or is counter to the actual needs of other members of society. That is, if in declining hearing the person begins to break social custom as illustrated in Figure 4.2, what happens? Ronayne and Wynne (1985) call it *stress*. They claim that stress

arises from the interaction between the person and the environment. More specifically, psychological stress arises from a particular relationship between the person and the environment, a relationship which is judged by the person to be demanding of the person's resources or is judged to threaten the person's sense of well-being in its most general sense. (2)

Stress occurs therefore when there is a conflict of view or need. At this point coping needs to occur. Ronayne and Wynne (1985) suggest three types of coping: *problem-focused* (e.g. admitting deafness at the outset of a conversation so that it reduces this conflict of view), *emotional* (e.g. having a good cry, or even denial of the problem) and *anticipatory* (e.g. good health and mental habits leading to a strong positive self-image so that one is in good shape to face stress). However, what is clear is that dissipation of stress is not solely in the hands of the individual. Other people can reduce the stress by perceiving the problem and taking appropriate action. But other people may be distanced from the event which is provoking stress and are therefore unable or unwilling to take steps to reduce stress. This might occur where the person is unemployed – those in control of jobs may be too distanced from this simple experience of unemployment. Supporting much of this is the personal-account literature which repeatedly seems to illustrate the stress occurring for the hearing-impaired.

We wish to propose that it is at the point or points when the stress created by attempts to resolve the conflict between personal needs for control and social norms for behaviour becomes significantly great that the hearing-impaired person seeks diagnosis and remediation. At that point, medical and audiological help is requested or made available or imposed on them. Where the hearing loss has arisen in an accident, of course, the first main period of traumatic stress will have been altered and the person moves from phase 1 directly to phase 3. In each of the phases there is a particular vocabulary reflecting perceptions of the whole process (Figure 4.4). In phase 3, questions of control are held in abeyance while crisis for those suddenly deafened and remediation for those with declining hearing has to be faced. In both cases, it is the start of rehabilitation, an ideal opportunity for a self-appraisal and an ideal starting point for the helping services. Unfortunately, this turns out mainly to be the provision of hearing aids and not support in the resolution of adjustment problems. That is not to say that hearing-aid provision does not solve the problems for some people or that surgery and medical treatment is not effective. It is simply the case that many people require more attention to the whole adjustment process.

In phase 4, the emphasis changes to helping and caring. As a prerequisite for most authors, the hearing-impaired must be 'made' to admit their problem:

Figure 4.4   The process of adjustment

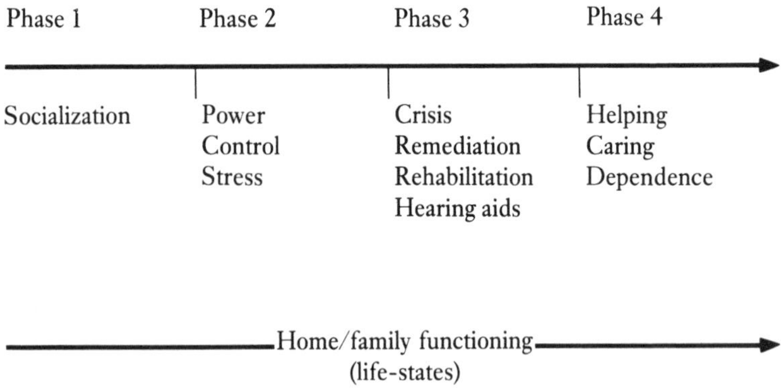

Phase 1	Phase 2	Phase 3	Phase 4
Socialization	Power Control Stress	Crisis Remediation Rehabilitation Hearing aids	Helping Caring Dependence

Home/family functioning (life-states)

When the hearing-impaired admit to themselves and, perhaps more importantly, to others, the fact of their impairment, the process of acceptance of the disability is begun, not only in the individual but also in the people he or she meets. The process of informing others, not only of the disability but also of the various communicative needs of the hearing disabled leads to an improved understanding and ultimately increased consideration of the hearing disabled person. (Ronayne and Wynne 1985; 20)

In view of the fact that the greater proportion of hearing-impaired people have not reached the point of diagnosis and referral, and given the very large percentage of our interviewees (over 70 per cent) who avoid disclosure, we consider this statement highly dubious and very likely to *create the stress* if applied by counsellors with no corresponding change in behaviour of other people. It is nevertheless a common perception of people around those with a hearing problem: 'He never admits he's deaf.' In fact, disclosure by the person almost certainly precipitates loss of control and a decrease in power and as a result is avoided by the individual. This avoidance of disclosure is completely different, we believe, from the psychological mechanism of denial where there is no personal recognition of the problem.

In the UK, there is not a large network of helping agencies for those with hearing loss. Blaxter's (1976) complex models of service provision and access are not applicable in the cases of most hearing-impaired people. Much of the thrust of Blaxter's argument is negative and McKnight (1981) makes it quite clear that service provision may itself be disabling. He states it quite starkly:

The service systems communicate three propositions to the client:
You are deficient
You are the problem
You have a collection of problems.

In terms of the interest of service systems and *their* needs, the propositions become:
We *need* deficiency
The economic unit we *need* is the individual
The productive economic unit we *need* is an individual with multiple deficiencies. (29)

For acquired hearing loss the proposition in the past has been: 'your problem is your hearing; your hearing aid can make you hear better;

we provide it and you wear it'. To be fair, Alpiner's (1980) view is not so simple but the service practicalities in the UK have meant that the major time has been spent on hearing aids. Schlesinger (1985) writing in the USA is very much in agreement that current helping tends to diminish power and limit choice and ultimately leads to an acceptance of helplessness. Both Schlesinger (1985) and Langer (1983) see the problem as most acute in the elderly, but the principles of denial of control are the same no matter when they appear. Oyer and Oyer (1985) talk about dependence and independence in this context.

We believe that the adjustment process occurs for hearing-impaired people without their necessarily having recourse to the helping agencies or individuals during phase 4. This is consistent with the earlier findings that hearing-impaired people do not think other people understand the problem. As a result adjustment to hearing loss in phase 4 is still a matter of determination of control and power even though the levels may have altered as a result of the better hearing provided by an aid.

The full picture is not complete without reference to the life-state of the individual, described by Oyer and Oyer (1985) in the context of family functioning. At home, at work, in familiar settings, the hearing-impaired person establishes the position desired. The level of control is negotiated and, through this, adjustment to hearing loss is regulated.

Adjustment then concerns change: conscious or unconscious, slight or great, immediate or long-term. It does *not* require the individual to declare the problem in public and does not require others to care. Our caring and our rehabilitation services need to establish from the beginning the individual's integrity and validity of choice in how the adjustment is to be managed. Ultimately, the adjustment cannot be viewed without the circumstances of life-state and unless we can evaluate attitudes and practices by others around we have very little basis for advising a hearing-impaired person.

From this picture we must now proceed to examine the interaction of the factors and to determine what meaningful strategies there are for change in people with hearing loss.

II

THE EFFECTS OF
HEARING LOSS

5

Studying acquired hearing loss

Given the extensive literature as reported in previous chapters and the particular needs for study as identified in Chapter 4 our examination of acquired hearing loss addressed itself directly to the question of adjustment, relationships, and the progressive phases of hearing loss. Bearing in mind the problems of sampling described in Chapter 2, we have chosen our population very carefully to reflect the principal features of UK society. Specifically, we have matched geographically to the population of the County of Avon and draw our population from this area.

The study was designed to examine the effects of acquired hearing loss on personal relationships. We set out to interview a sample of those who had acquired a hearing loss in adult life and who were within the age range 20–60 years. In addition, since the interviews were conducted at home, we requested the participation of 'others' living at home. Normally this would be a partner or close relative. Since the hearing loss can be seen to affect other people at home, the interview concentrated on relationships: communication, 'hearing tactics' (the application of practical strategies by the hearing-impaired person), direct effects on personal contacts, decision-making, the way the hearing-impaired person presented him/herself to strangers, and apparently minor features of home life such as increased noise levels created by and for the hearing-impaired person.

None of these areas had been adequately explored in research using anything like a normal sample of the population. If we were able to collect this information it would be of great value to all providing agencies.

Our aim could then be said to be the exploration of adjustment and change in personal relations resulting from hearing loss within the

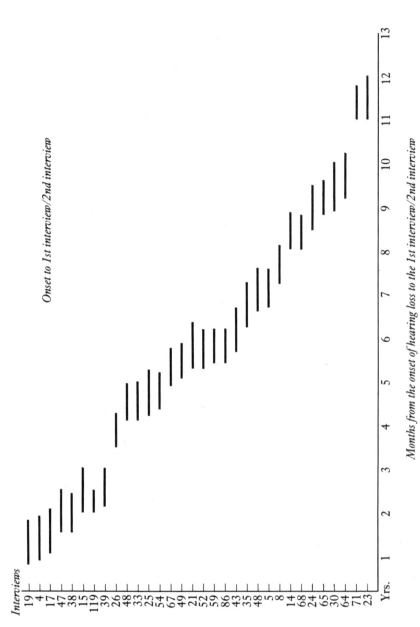

Figure 5.1 First to second interviews

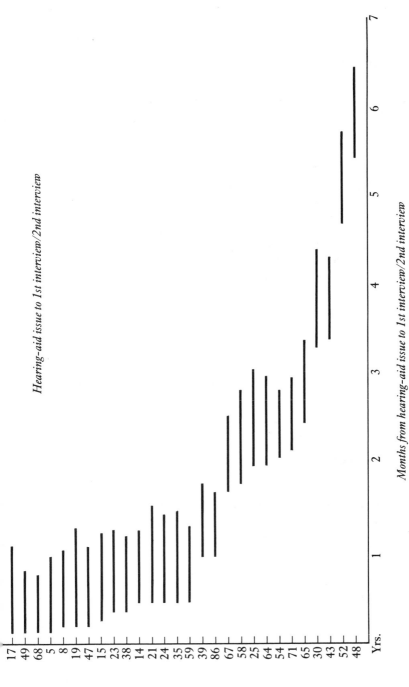

Figure 5.2 First to second interviews

home unit. In practical terms, the aims required us to overcome three problems:

1 obtaining access to a representative population;
2 constructing an adequate interview framework;
3 ensuring the cooperation of all 'families'.

The full details on these aspects of the study appear in Appendix 1. They illustrate how it was possible to match a hearing-impaired sample to the population as a whole and avoid the major problems of middle-class and sex bias. The sample was drawn from audiology clinics, direct contacts, and our own records; in addition a pre-diagnostic group was included who had a measured hearing loss but had not attended a clinic or gone for treatment.

People were interviewed early in the project and then ten months later a sub-set were reinterviewed. This sub-set consisted of those in the earliest stage of adjustment following diagnosis. Figures 5.1 and 5.2 show the months from hearing loss to the first and second interviews.

CHARACTERISTICS OF THE POPULATION

Our initial concerns centred on a series of sample variables:

(a) Recency

Our analysis of phases led us to try to identify the period into which the individual fell. Not surprisingly this proved very difficult to establish. At the outset, we had imagined that people could be classified according to recency and we largely concentrated on phase 4 analysis. As it became clear that adjustment could occur earlier we widened the sample. Table 5.1 shows the overall distribution in terms of the proposed phases. This is a *post hoc* analysis and the major part of our work is reported in terms of the original recency categories.

Since our study was of development in hearing loss, we interviewed a sub-sample of thirty-four on a second occasion (Table A.3 in the Appendix). This consisted of people with recent onsets of hearing loss and was an attempt to understand early adjustment.

Establishing the recency of hearing loss is a problem. We asked directly 'How old were you when you developed a hearing loss?' The average age reported was 41.5 years (SD 11.6 years). When inter-

Table 5.1   The sample in relation to 'phases'

Phase 2	Phase 3	Phase 4		
No hearing aid	No hearing aid	Hearing aid Diagnosed (mths)		
No diagnosis	Diagnosed	0–23	24–71	72
17	20	25	29	32

viewed ten months later three people (out of thirty-two) had altered their views all towards a younger onset (40 years to 30 years, 35 to 20 years and a massive 52 to 18 years). A further eighteen people had altered their responses by up to 3 years. That is, a total of 56 per cent of this sub-sample had altered their considered date of onset by the time of the second interview. Onset has therefore to be treated with some caution as a measure.

(b)   Hearing loss

As we have reported in previous studies (Wood and Kyle 1983, Kyle and Wood 1984) hearing loss is usually gradual and on the whole mild for the majority of people. Relatively few people have profound acquired losses. We used an 8-point scale which is now commonly called the Gallaudet scale of hearing-loss rating and we requested people to complete ratings both with and without aids. The distribution is shown in Table 5.2. The great majority of our sample have mild losses. For the pre-diagnostic sample 7 per cent have more serious losses while 11 per cent of those whose onset was more than six years ago have serious losses.

Estimated hearing losses of these ratings come from Schein and Delk (1974). For a sub-sample of the population (n=37) we obtained audiograms from the audiology clinic and correlation between measured hearing loss and rating without an aid is high (r=0.66, df= 35, p<.001). This is likely to be an underestimate of correlation since the hearing tests may have been carried out some time before the interviews. When we compare our interviewees' estimates with their actual hearing loss there is close correspondence to the hearing-loss figures provided by Schein and Delk (1974) (Table 5.3).

Table 5.2   Distribution of hearing loss by Gallaudet Scale

	No aid %	*With aid* %	*Estimated hearing loss (dB)*
Can't hear anything at all.	2.4	2.3	120+
Can you hear loud noises?	1.6	–	109+
Can you usually tell one kind of noise from another?	1.6	1.2	89.6–109
Can you usually tell the sound of speech from other sounds and noises?	1.6	1.2	70.6–89.5
Can you usually hear and understand a person if he speaks loudly into your better ear?	17.1	–	52.8–70.5
Can you usually hear and understand what a person says without seeing his face *if he shouts* to you from across a quiet room?	50.4	7.0	36.2–52.7
Can you usually hear and understand what a person says without seeing his face *if he talks in a normal voice* to you from across a quiet room?	19.5	88.4	20.8–36.1
Can you usually hear and understand what a person says without seeing his face *if he whispers* to you from across a quiet room?	5.7	–	5.0–20.7
	100 (n=123)	100 (n=86)	

Table 5.3   Correspondence of hearing-loss ratings with
Gallaudet Scale

	Our sample measured better ear average dB	Gallaudet Scale dB
Can't hear anything to Can tell speech from other sounds	64.25	>70.6
Can hear loud speech in better ear	48.38	61.65
Can hear a shout without lip reading across a room	46.43	44.45
Can hear normal speech without lip reading across a room	29.44	28.45
	n=37	

When we look at recency in relation to deafness as measured by audiograms we find that those with older audiograms appear to be more deaf, though we have only measurement for a few of those with the longest period since onset. When we look at rated hearing loss on the Gallaudet Scale we find those people who are most recent (under 12 months), compared with those recencies of over six years, have fewer with serious losses (4 per cent as compared to 11 per cent in the 70dB+ range) and more with milder losses (29 per cent as compared to 8 per cent in the 20–36dB range). Statistical analysis of the scale shows that there is a trend towards more deafness in the longest *recencies* although this does not relate to actual onset of hearing loss. The significant difference is between the pre-diagnostic group and the others taken as a whole. More of the pre-diagnostic group have milder losses but they are represented in each category.

It is possible that there are underlying differences between those who are pre-diagnostic; they may have a higher than average level of conductive hearing loss; they may also have variable periods of hearing loss alternating with some alleviation. We have no easy way of determining the validity of this. However, it is perceived continuing hearing loss which we have taken into account, and these causal factors may weigh less heavily in the overall analysis.

(c) Sex

Because the pre-diagnosis group were all male, the sample population is skewed towards males (67.5 per cent). If we consider only the phases 3 and 4 population, the population is more balanced (57.4 per cent males). This makes the overall composition on this variable almost identical to Thomas's (1984) groups and more weighted towards men than Kyle and Wood (1983) and Kyle, Wood, and Jones (1983). There are differences in employment by sex (Table 5.4) with women more likely to be out of paid work and to be in less skilled jobs.

Table 5.4   Distribution of own job by sex (%) (n=123)

	Men (n=83)	Women (n=40)
Professional/managerial	18	10
Junior non-manual	23	10
Skilled manual	28	0
Semi- or unskilled	20	35
Unemployed	6	5
Housewife/retired/other	5	40
	100	100

(d) Age

The overall age was 48.4 years with women interviewed younger than men (45.6 as compared to 49.7 years). The reason for this is in the inclusion of the older pre-diagnostic group. Excluding these, male age drops to 47.9 years, closer to the female age. The pre-diagnostic group's average age is 56.8 years while the other recency categories are closely clustered around the mid-40s. There is no systematic variation of age and rated hearing loss.

(e) Marital status

Of the total sample 86 per cent were married, 4 per cent divorced or separated, 2 per cent widowed and 7 per cent single.

(f) Job

After considerable deliberation we chose to match 'households' to the population rather than 'own job'. Most demographic statistics are based on households and socio-economic grouping tends to be more accurately reflected by *head of household's* occupation. In this study we are more concerned with how the family copes and so chose to deal with the sample in this way. This still remains a rather crude way to match to the general population as one might claim that marital status, number of children, and type of house are all useful aspects in determining family position and we are very aware of the shortcomings of this categorization, especially for classifying women's position in the labour market. However, short of mounting a national study it would have been impossible to interview a balanced quota. We have already shown the classification by head of household (Tables A.1 and A.2). The distribution by own job is shown in Table 5.5.

Table 5.5 Comparison of own job and head of household's

	Own job		Head of household	
	n	*%*	*n*	*%*
Professional	11	8.9	11	8.9
Employer/manager	8	6.5	11	8.9
Junior intermediate	23	18.7	25	20.3
Skilled manual (own account)	23	18.7	34	27.7
Semi-skilled (personal services)	20	16.3	17	13.8
Unskilled manual	9	7.3	8	6.5
Unemployed	7	5.7	5	4.2
Retired	7	5.7	8	6.5
Widow(er)	2	1.6	3	2.4
Student	1	0.8	1	0.8
Housewife	12	9.8	–	–
	123	100.0	123	100.0

(g) Housing

We asked for a simple classification of house type. Four types were used. People lived in detached houses (12.2 per cent), semi-detached (41.5 per cent), terraced (38.2 per cent), or flats (8.1 per cent). We have been unable so far to compare these adequately to the Avon population.

(h)   People at home

As an indication of family type we asked about the number of people at home. We found of our total sample that 3 per cent lived alone; in the others there were two people (28 per cent), three people (29 per cent), four people (30 per cent), five people (6 per cent), six people (2 per cent) and seven people (1 per cent). In comparison to overall census figures we are well down on number of people living alone but this arises because of our targeting on people aged 20–60 years. There are no age-related statistics for the census.

(i)   Hearing-aid possession

Perhaps surprisingly we were at times given conflicting information as to hearing-aid possession. Occasionally the other person at home would inform us that the hearing-impaired person did have an aid but never used it. As we had already examined use of hearing aids in a previous study (Kyle and Wood 1984) we chose not to question people on the extent of use. At the first interview, 72 per cent had a hearing aid or 91 per cent excluding the pre-diagnostic group. Of the sample who participated in both interviews, 88 per cent had hearing aids the first time and 94 per cent on the second occasion.

Table 5.6   Age left school (%) (n=123)

14 years	15 years	16 years	17+
27.6	35.0	23.6	13.8

(j)   Education

Table 5.6 shows the age at which the sample had left school. A considerable number left school before what is the norm nowadays. Consistent with this a very large group left without qualifications: O levels (72 per cent), A levels (87 per cent) or CSE's (98 per cent). Nevertheless the A level pass rate was as high as recent averages in the 1970s of 13 per cent, so the group as a whole was not dissimilar to the general population. Forty-one per cent had received no further training after school while 26 per cent had gone through apprenticeships and a further 22 per cent had had on-the-job training.

(k)   Description of themselves

We asked people how they viewed themselves and gave them a list of adjectives (Table 5.7). The majority were prepared to agree with hard-of-hearing as an acceptable term but it was hardly an overwhelming majority. The group seemed unprepared to commit themselves to a particular 'label'. When we considered only those people who identified one adjective as being appropriate then the majority picture shifted towards 'slightly hard-of-hearing'. It is clear that this group saw themselves as mildly hearing-impaired and this is consistent with their direct self-ratings of hearing loss.

Table 5.7   Adjectives used to describe oneself (% agreeing) (n=123)

	Diagnosed sample (n=94)	Pre-diagnostic sample (n=29)
Deaf	13	13
Hard of hearing	59	53
Slightly hard of hearing	42	41
Profoundly deaf	5	3
Partially hearing	40	34
Hearing-impaired	30	28

HEARING PARTICIPANTS

The average age of spouses and partners who contributed data to the computer analysis was 37 years, though for those direct comparisons of hearing and hearing-impaired the average age after excluding children was 47. Complementary to the male bias in the hearing-impaired group, 68 per cent of the hearing sample was female. The most commonly used adjective by hearing people was 'hard-of-hearing'. Job characteristics, not surprisingly, follow the pattern for hearing people.

It can be seen that our population is not perfectly balanced and there are difficulties in exactly using the phase structure we have proposed so far. Some of the characteristics of these phases have only become apparent through analysis and this analysis has largely followed our initial primitive recency categories. These have the advantage of being readily matched to other research populations and have the simplicity of relating to hearing-aid fittings. The unevenness caused by the problems of establishing hearing-aid use we believe to be small overall and feel confident that an analysis of those who have been officially diagnosed and those who are pre-diagnostic is still of considerable value.

Having examined some of the demographic variables for the population it is now possible to begin to consider the effects of hearing loss. The next chapters describe in detail our results and their meaning in relation to the variables so far examined.

6

Bringing hearing loss home

'He's a good husband really, he doesn't drink or go with other women – but he just doesn't understand this (hearing loss). We're poles apart really – I think it's a lot to do with my deafness'. (83)

The hearing impairment seen through the eyes of the hearing-impaired can be seen here in the feelings that arise about living together when one person has a hearing loss.

To examine home life as our first step in the analysis of hearing impairment is probably to tackle the most difficult area first. Not only do we need to chart the series of events occurring for the individual but also the changing perception and attitude towards them. What complicates the picture, of course, is that all this occurs in the framework of personal relations and most important of these are the relationships at home. What this means in practical terms is that we need to understand the views of others in the home to determine the effect of the home setting. What we will attempt to do here and repeat in later sections is to present the perspective of the hearing-impaired and then to examine how this matches the other members of the household. Where necessary and appropriate we will introduce sections from our transcripts of the interviews to try to illustrate the points to be made (the number in brackets refers to Appendix 2). Our examination of home life will deal with the events in the life of the hearing-impaired person (in each phase), the attitudes to hearing loss and home life, and the perceptions of the effects of hearing loss at home for partners and children.

HEARING LOSS: EVENTS

To tackle this part we need to separate the reports on the different phases of our model in Chapter 4.

Phase 2: onset of hearing loss till diagnosis

'I noticed my hearing going in the army, he [the sergeant major] used to give orders, that lot would go that way and I'd still be going straight ahead! They sent me off for tests' (67). This man was very forcefully alerted to his declining hearing; for most people it is a more gradual process over a number of years.

A more typical reaction was one man, driven to the doctor by his family's reaction:

Table 6.1   Situations which happened a lot which indicated hearing loss (%) (n=123)

	Pre-diagnosis	Recency (yrs)		
		0–2	2–5	6+
Turning up the TV or radio	52	79	53	75
Asking people to repeat things	59	82	60	78
Asking people to shout/talk loudly	28	14	20	39
Asking people to speak more slowly	21	4	10	22
Asking people to speak more clearly	21	4	17	19
Complaining about a bad line or people talking quietly on the telephone	35	43	20	25
Complaining about people mumbling at meetings	32	47	29	24
Being told to lower your voice when outside in public	24	4	3	3
Not hearing the door-bell or someone calling	45	25	13	17
Missing out on conversation at home	45	29	30	31
Not knowing where sounds were coming from	35	14	27	17

I was just a fool to have gone without it [hearing aid] so long. I suppose you could put it as pride and laziness ... in the end it became so bad, the wife kept shouting at me and I couldn't hear, so I thought well, I've got to do something about this ... in the end I had *no option* but to do something about it, and of course the volume of the television was driving my wife up the wall. (49)

We used four groups within our total interviewed sample: pre-diagnostic, within two years of diagnosis, from two to five years, and six years and over. Our first consideration was to know which features alerted people to the fact that they had a hearing loss (Table 6.1).

Direct comparisons of the pre-diagnostic group with the others is more difficult because of the sex and job differences but some differences are marked (Table 6.1).

The principal events which prompted self-diagnosis were the television and radio volume and the requests for repetition. None of the other situations come anywhere near these in frequency. The concern therefore is not simply with interaction but also with links to the environment. Perception of others at fault still occurs in a significant group with both complaints about people mumbling at meetings or talking quietly on the phone. None of the differences arising between the recency categories reaches statistical significance in chi-square analysis (n=94). There is no evidence therefore for differential recall in these groups. There are some interesting differences according to the sex of the hearing-impaired person. Women were more aware of turning the television volume up a lot (75 per cent compared to 60 per cent men), of asking people to repeat (80 per cent compared to 65 per cent), and of missing conversation at home (45 per cent compared to 28 per cent), though the differences do not reach statistical significance. Men are less likely to complain about telephone lines (29 per cent rarely as compared to women only 8 per cent rarely, p<.01), less likely to have had problems with the doorbell (25 per cent rarely as compared to 5 per cent rarely, p<.01) and less likely to have problems with sound localization (30 per cent compared to 8 per cent, p<.01). Not surprisingly there is a consistent effect of rated hearing loss. The more deaf the person is the more likely they are to report each of these situations.

However, there is evidence of difference in the situation which occurred most frequently (Table 6.2). Those over two years of recency remember having to ask people to repeat things while those less than two years are more likely to report missing conversation at home (p<.01).

Women are equally likely to report missing conversation (48 per cent) as having to have things repeated (45 per cent) and this is significantly different from men who claim that it is repetition (70 per cent of the time) which is the most frequent.

This difference is also seen in hearing-loss comparisons where the more deaf the person is the more likely there is to be a report of missing conversation at home. Those with milder losses report asking for repetitions. There is a massive difference also by job (Table 6.3), those in skilled manual jobs being much more likely to identify repetitions as the trigger which made them more aware (90 per cent).

For the pre-diagnostic group the distribution is more similar to the longer recency groups. Perhaps the most significant aspect to these situations was the likelihood of being discovered. Fifty-three per cent felt that other people had realized their problems (though this was related to the extent of hearing loss – the greater the loss the more likely people were to realize). The majority (57 per cent) found others had commented 'you must be deaf!' but there are large and significant differences between those most recently diagnosed and the others (p<.01). A full 75 per cent of those diagnosed over six years ago found people had said this to them.

The key question of course, is, how did the hearing-impaired person react? (Table 6.3). The answer seems to be 'differently

Table 6.2   The situation which happened most frequently (%) (n=119)

Situation	Pre-diagnostic	Recency (yrs)		
		0–2	*2–5*	*6+*
Turning up TV or radio	23	4	0	0
Asking people to repeat things	62	32	73	75
Complaining about mumbling at meetings	8	18	3	3
Missing out on conversation at home	7	46	24	22
Total	100	100	100	100

76

depending on when you became deaf'. Whether we have just different levels of recall here is not clear but longer time since diagnosis makes people more likely to say they avoided the situation (p<.01), adjusted, or admitted the deafness. The more deaf, the more likely avoidance was and the more likely they were to be angry. Women were also more likely to be angry and more likely to be frustrated. Men were more likely to joke about it. As we can see in Table 6.3 there are differences between the pre-diagnostic group and the others. They appear to be much less affected by the problem of people's reaction and much more likely to joke about hearing loss. In terms of overall coping only 3 per cent felt they had coped 'very well' with this situation and the majority (54 per cent) felt that they had not coped. Men seemed to have coped slightly better than women. There is no difference according to hearing loss in their rated coping.

Table 6.3   Reactions to people's responses to perceived hearing loss (% adopting this strategy) (n=123)

	Pre-diagnostic	Recency (yrs)		
		0–2	2–5	6+
Try to avoid situation	13	0	21	50
Try to adjust to others	24	79	93	92
Become angry	5	46	41	36
Feel frustrated	20	75	55	78
Admit deafness (jokingly)	62	4	17	20

With this sort of profile we would expect people to try to overcome the frustration and discuss the matter at home. At home the matter was usually raised by the hearing-impaired person (Table 6.4). Relatively few people mentioned it at work. The pattern is perhaps as one would predict. People with an acquired loss begin to notice it by having to ask people to repeat, because of problems in regulating sound in the environment. They try to adjust to others without disclosing their own concerns about deafness. When this concern eventually comes to the surface, it happens at home and the hearing-impaired person is likely to broach the subject.

Table 6.4   First discussion of hearing loss begins (%) (n=119)

| | Pre-diagnostic | Recency (yrs) | | |
		0–2	2–5	6+
By hearing-impaired at home	85	89	79	94
By hearing-impaired at work	0	0	10	6
By a member of the family	15	11	7	0
By someone at work	0	0	4	0
By another	0	0	0	0
Total	100	100	100	100

Phase 3: diagnosis

We asked people what had been the final trigger for the visit to their doctor about their hearing. The vast majority (83 per cent) claimed it as a result of the situations above and not, as is sometimes assumed, as a result of family pressure (9 per cent). A further 7 per cent felt it arose in a general concern they had. So a full 90 per cent felt that the decision to consult a GP was their own. From that point of decision the time gap until actual consultation took place was surprisingly long. Forty-three per cent overall said it was several years before they went to their doctor about it. Only 9 per cent went within weeks of the realization. Those people most recently diagnosed were most likely to have waited several years (70 per cent). There was some tendency for more-deaf people to go more quickly but this was by no means a direct relationship. Fifty per cent of those with losses over 70dB were likely to have waited over a year.

Usually the loss was sufficiently severe for the doctor to pass them on for specialist advice but not necessarily immediately. Fifty-eight per cent were recognized as hearing-impaired at the first visit but 24 per cent had to go three or more times before their hearing loss was identified and specialist treatment suggested. Of those who were put off by the doctor 61 per cent reported they felt reassured by this. At this stage there was very little secrecy and people at home knew about the visit to the doctor (in 97 per cent of cases).

Wood and Kyle (1983) have already described the transition from doctor to audiology clinics and shown the great lack of information. On

78

this occasion we attempted to probe the events and the responses which occured. At the point of referral, the vast majority was relieved (87 per cent), few were surprised (29 per cent) and most were worried (71 per cent). Those whose hearing loss was most severe seemed to be more relieved as one would expect. Although people also saw others at home as being relieved to the same degree as the hearing-impaired person (83 per cent), they were much less worried (46 per cent) and much less surprised (3 per cent).

We found that 6 per cent said their doctor told them about hearing loss while 49 per cent were told by ENT consultants and 45 per cent by the audiologist. However, information is expected and the manner in which it is given is of some importance. Most felt that allowances were made for their hearing loss – by speaking simply (86 per cent), by speaking clearly (88 per cent), by repeating when asked (89 per cent) – but few had information written down (20 per cent). There was a slight trend towards people with more recent experience being slightly more favourably treated. However, those with a milder hearing loss seemed to have more favourable memories than those with the more severe losses.

Most people were given some indication of the nature or cause of their hearing loss. However, one-third were given no information. The crux of the matter was whether the explanation was understood, and the vast majority (92 per cent) did understand the explanation when it was given. There were no underlying effects of recency, hearing loss, or level of education in this.

In this section, the results are very much in line with Wood and Kyle (1983) in that fewer problems exist than in the past in understanding what transpires at the audiology clinic. Nevertheless, there is still a sizeable proportion who have a considerable struggle to convince their doctor of their problems.

RESPONSES TO DIAGNOSIS

Responses varied from contemplating suicide to seeing hearing loss as an expected part of ageing. The way diagnosis was made and how people were informed was important. Depression immediately after diagnosis seemed to be reported more readily by those whose hearing had actually improved since that time either as a result of an operation or amelioration in their condition. Chapter 9, on perceptions of hearing loss, examines these responses in detail.

Individuals and families devised the strategies for coping with this first stage of seeking help, going through the system and being labelled hard-of-hearing. What emerges is the extent to which these stages are shared by all those involved in the process. Signs of 'making an effort' and perseverance in firstly seeking help and then wearing a hearing aid (if one was issued) were important in family outcome. Equally those with hearing loss presented a picture which explained or justified their perceived lack of effort by the hearing members of the family.

Phase 4: wearing a hearing aid

The majority of our sample had reached phase 4 and had begun to wear an aid (89 per cent). We asked them about their initial reactions to it and how the people at home coped. Those with the most recent hearing aids found their hearing improved (56 per cent said 'a lot' in the first recency category but only 27 per cent in the recency group between two and five years). This view about the help from a hearing aid seemed closely related to hearing loss. Of those with the most serious losses (>70dB) *none* felt their hearing had been improved 'a lot' while 54 per cent of those with hearing losses in the range 36–52dB felt it had helped 'a lot'. In other hearing-loss groups the improvement fell between these two extremes. It seems clear that the particular hearing-aid provision in this area works best for those with mild losses. Those people with less education (i.e. who left school at 14 years old) were more likely to have benefited 'a lot' from their hearing aid. Both men and women claim to benefit to the same degree.

In terms of confidence as to how others would adjust to the hearing problems, most people were positive. The major variable here seems to be degree of loss with those with severe hearing losses (>70dB) much less confident. This obviously produces a basis for discussion at home and some discussion of required adaptation was undertaken. Where applicable 82 per cent discussed 'how to talk to someone with a hearing aid' with their spouse, but only 13 per cent with their children. These were the largest groups. Twenty per cent talked to parents and 14 per cent to siblings. Women were more likely to discuss with their partners (90 per cent) than men were with theirs (76 per cent), though there was no difference in relation to discussions with children (both under 15 per cent).

In an ideal world these people at home would understand the need for hearing-aid use and be helpful in its use. The majority received encouragement 'often' or 'very often' from people at home (54 per cent). However, one in six received no encouragement at all and this was greatest where hearing loss was least (37 per cent where loss was less than 21dB). Presumably this was where the least difference was found between wearing and not wearing the aid. Women were much more likely to receive 'no encouragement' to wear their aid than men. When we asked a key question for understanding as to whether the partner tried the aid, only 15 per cent had tried the aid. Male hearing partners were much more likely to have tried the aid (25 per cent) as compared to female hearing partners (8 per cent). We find this figure rather worrying. Since we have discovered that much of the stigma revolving round hearing-aid use and many of the reported stressful experiences related to hearing-aid use (e.g. volume levels) it is very surprising that hearing-impaired people are not encouraged to get their partners to try the aid so that they can experience the sound. At the very least 'dummy' aids should be available to family members (i.e. on loan to the hearing-impaired) so that they can experience some of the classic problems of hearing-aid use, e.g. sound localization, incidental noise, and the basic change in sound characteristics produced by the aid. Given that most people received encouragement to use the aid it is clear that this is a 'try-it-we-think-you-need-it' type of support, rather than a realistic form of understanding.

Nevertheless in the first few weeks of hearing-aid use we found that most people felt satisfied with their family's response and did not suggest any further strategies which the families could have followed.

Hearing-aid use even at home is still a question of 'which situation?' Most people had positive experiences and found some improvement. However, there is a pattern of application consistent with that found in Kyle and Wood (1984) (Table 6.5). Hearing-aid usefulness seems to be greatest for those with mildest losses. Improvements as a result of the aid are much less when hearing losses are greater than 71dB on the Gallaudet scale. Considering our results in the previous chapter which indicate our groups may be over-rating their degree of hearing loss at this level, it is a somewhat worrying finding.

There are a series of other questions we asked about family responses, separate from hearing-aid use, but these deal more with interaction with others and responses to it. We shall discuss these in Chapter 7 when dealing with social life. For the moment we wish to deal only with stated attitudes to home life and to deafness.

Table 6.5 **Situations where use of hearing aid allowed the person to cope a lot better (%) (n=89)**

| | Hearing loss | | | | |
	>71dB	53–70dB	36–52dB	<35dB	all
Watching TV	43	39	60	58	55
Talking to one other person	0	23	56	54	46
Talking to several	0	15	21	23	19
Using the telephone	0	8	6	0	5
Hearing doorbell	0	0	8	8	6
Talking to callers at the door	0	8	10	8	8
Locating sounds	0	0	4	8	4

ATTITUDES TO HOME LIFE WITH HEARING LOSS

In this, as in the next section, we are interested in showing differences between the pre-diagnostic group and those who *are* 'hearing-impaired'. We asked for simple scale judgements of agreement/disagreement on a number of statements (Table 6.6). Two striking differences emerge. The pre-diagnostic group are clearly suffering from the family's being unaware of the hearing loss. Eighty-four per cent feel little consideration is given to them. Post-diagnosis, the situation is much more positive. At the same time the pre-diagnostic group feel that social life may continue after hearing loss while perhaps there is a more realistic view from those whose losses are diagnosed.

We also asked about activities related to deafness and again there is a marked difference between the post-diagnostic group and the others (Table 6.7). Most surprising is perhaps the fact that in the pre-diagnosis group none have ever watched a television programme on deafness. This is all the more striking when we see the implied level of hearing loss in the pre-diagnosis group (Table 6.8). Both groups are very similar in the extent to which they ask for repetitions and more clarity in speech. In fact, the pre-diagnostic group show the characteristics of those with a recognized loss.

Table 6.6 Attitudes to hearing loss at home (% who agree or strongly agree with the statements)

	Pre-diagnostic (n=25)	Diagnosed (n=94)
Other family members seldom try to ensure that the hard-of-hearing person can follow what is being said	84	46
If a family member is hard-of-hearing, then the others will adjust their social lives to help	60	54
The family should jointly discuss how to help the hard-of-hearing person	92	99
The stress felt by people who are hard-of-hearing makes them more irritable	92	93
A hearing loss means you cannot continue your social life as before	24	58
People generally understand the problems of deafness	16	9

Table 6.7 Activities related to deafness engaged in (%)

	Pre-diagnostic (n=28)	Diagnosed (n=94)
Read leaflets on deafness	0	53
Gone to lip-reading class	0	6
Watched TV programme on deafness	0	56
Joined a club for hard-of-hearing	0	4

Table 6.8 **Responses to hearing loss 'when you are talking at home do you ask them to ...?' (% often or very often)**

	Pre-diagnostic (n=28)	Diagnosed (n=94)
Repeat things	82	84
Speak more loudly	39	55
Speak more clearly	29	28
Write things down	0	6
Make gestures	0	6

ATTITUDES TO HEARING LOSS IN GENERAL

In 1981, Bunting published a questionnaire study of people interviewed about deafness. They were chosen for their typicality as members of the public. They seemed to show more insight into deafness than expected but at the same time were rather negative. We compared our hearing and hard-of-hearing people with the original 'normative' results reported by Bunting (Table 6.8).

The most interesting aspect of the comparison between our hearing-impaired interviewees and the hearing norms is their similarity. There is no obvious difference between hearing-impaired and hearing partners and more strikingly no obvious difference between hearing-impaired and the general population (Bunting 1981).

There are virtually no significant differences between hard-of-hearing and hearing family members on individual items but overall, when we add the items correcting for the positive/negative direction of statements and excluding neutral ones, we find our hearing-impaired people more antagonistic to other deaf people and more negative about their capabilities (Tables 6.9 and 6.10). Neither result quite reaches significance but is noticeable and surprising. Looking at the overall attitudinal variables we find hearing-impaired men are significantly more negative about hearing loss than women in scale 1 ($p<.05$) though the scale 2 difference does not reach significance. There are no differences by recency, hearing loss, or job. The sex difference is interesting because we find it also among hearing partners – males are significantly more negative (scale 1, $p<.01$). Combining families by subtracting hearing-impaired from hearing member's attitudinal score simply heightens this difference on scale 1.

Table 6.9 **Scale 1 mean attitudinal response to each statement in deaf and hearing people (1 = agree; 5 = disagree)**

	Hearing-impaired (n=97)	Hearing (n=97)	Bunting (1981) (n<500)
I feel sympathetic towards deaf people, and help them whenever possible	1.40	1.23	1.49
I don't mind talking to deaf people, but I find them hard going	2.39	2.32	2.50
I find it embarrassing to talk to deaf people in public	3.97	3.80	4.05
I am more considerate in dealing with deaf people than with hearing people	1.97	1.99	2.05
I try to avoid talking to deaf people as it makes me feel self-conscious	4.16	4.22	4.37
I would treat deaf people in the same way as I would treat anyone else	1.59	1.72	1.66
I get impatient in dealing with deaf people as it takes so long to get through to them	3.94	3.60	3.88
I feel inadequate in dealing with deaf people	3.73	3.51	3.57
I find deaf people irritating as conversation with them is so difficult	3.91	3.93	3.89
I find deaf people generally more friendly and easier to talk to than hearing people	2.69	3.02	2.89
I find it easier to talk to deaf people if I know in advance they are deaf	1.84	1.93	1.91
I don't know enough about deafness to know how to talk to deaf people	3.30	3.14	2.79

Table 6.10   Scale 2 mean attitudinal response to each statement in deaf and hearing people (1 = agree; 5 = disagree)

	Hearing-impaired (n=97)	Hearing (n=97)	Bunting (1981) (n=<500)
Deaf people feel very isolated because of the problems they have in communicating	1.56	1.63	2.08
Deaf people seem to have fewer interests than hearing people	3.14	3.30	3.35
Deaf people have more difficulty in coping with everyday activities around the home than hearing people	2.76	3.15	3.45
Deaf people are less likely to take part in sports and games than hearing people	3.54	3.38	2.88
Deaf people seem generally less intelligent than hearing people	4.51	4.29	4.09
Deaf people face more hazards in travelling and getting about than hearing people	1.81	2.03	1.77
Deaf people are unable to keep up with what's going on in the world through the news media	3.34	3.65	3.65
Deaf people seem to have more than the usual number of *other* physical complaints	3.93	3.92	3.87
Deaf people have more problems in banks, post offices, and shops than hearing people do	1.84	2.39	2.10
Deaf people have more difficulty getting on with people at work than hearing people do	2.71	2.88	2.62
Deaf people frequently seem to behave rather oddly	4.11	4.18	3.53

We see also that if any differences exist between our sample, then people with a hearing loss are more negative about hearing impairment. In effect, it means the general population may overestimate aspects of the deafness self-image even though their assessment of real ability or functioning may be realistic. Hearing-impaired people have begun to 'be disabled'.

TINNITUS

This was an area which caused considerable stress for the hearing-impaired person. The problems of tinnitus for adaptation to hearing loss is related to its disturbance of sleep and disturbance of a sense of ease and relaxation generally. For some people tinnitus was 'the main problem'. One man said 'I can live with the hearing loss but the tinnitus is driving me mad' (39). For this couple in their 40s it had meant sleeping in separate rooms as the husband found he slept very badly because of severe tinnitus. For both husband and wife this was seen as a depressing step to take, which although they felt it was a necessary one meant an increasing lack of physical and emotional closeness.

Tinnitus puts an additional amount of stress on someone who is very often struggling to keep up with conversation anyway. An overlay of noise ranging from 'buzzing noises' to a 'full scale band playing' or 'a jet engine revving up to take off', can be the final stress factor which makes it impossible to cope. But it can be in conjunction with other factors that tinnitus is problematic. Not being able to sleep, as a result of tinnitus, causes fatigue, irritability during the day, disrupts the rest of the family, and may cause marital problems. Nighttime tinnitus causing loss of sleep means lying awake worrying and becoming anxious. A 'side-effect' of tinnitus, which was even more distressing for one respondent (but mentioned by others), was the fear of 'going mad'. 'Hearing things' is a popular way of describing certain types of mental illness and for one respondent in particular whose mother had been in a psychiatric hospital it was a very real fear. This fear is sometimes reinforced by doctors prescribing tranquillizers, such as valium, as a 'remedy' for tinnitus. If this is given without any explanation there is a belief on the part of the patient that the tinnitus is not being taken seriously as a symptom and is being construed by the doctor as 'nerves'. The most common response from GPs was that 'you've just got to live with it' which patients often interpreted as a lack of concern

Table 6.11   Comparison of deaf and hearing people in their response 'it happened a lot' (%) (n=97)

	Pre-diagnostic		Diagnosed	
	Hearing-impaired	Hearing	Hearing-impaired	Hearing
Turning up the TV or radio	48	43	69	72
Asking people to repeat things	55	59	70	70
Asking people to shout/ talk loudly	26	21	27	49
Asking people to speak more slowly	17	6	13	40
Asking people to speak more clearly	17	6	15	46
Complaining about a bad line or people talking quietly on the telephone	21	16	27	33
Complaining about mumbling at meetings	22	11	33	38
Being told to lower your voice when outside in public	26	37	2	32
Not hearing the door-bell or someone calling	40	40	18	69
Missing out on conversation at home	40	35	30	60
Not knowing where sounds were coming from	30	15	19	49

on the part of the doctor. For people who lived with constant noise, both day and night, this is not very reassuring. One man said his tinnitus was 'bloody horrible, like a permanent brass band effect' (50). It is clearly an important factor in trying to estimate the effect of an acquired hearing loss on people's lives.

Tinnitus is, like the extent of hearing loss, a factor which we may be unable to remedy directly. It is a variable factor which has to be taken into account in building the picture of the interaction at home.

LIVING WITH A HEARING-IMPAIRED PERSON

Perhaps the key part to the study concerns the views of people living at home. In their independent interview, hearing and hearing-impaired people were asked the same questions. One would predict that the degree to which there was concurrence in their responses was an indication of the adjustment level. As we have seen in the section on attitudes people are close in their general views about deafness. When we asked about phase 1, hearing-impaired people generally identified television and repetitions as significant. However, the hearing person is likely to identify many more circumstances in which hearing loss is apparent (Table 6.11). Significantly, it is the effects on the hearing-impaired which show clearest differences – speaking too loudly, not hearing the door-bell, missing conversation, and so on. Also important is the fact that the pre-diagnostic group are much more in agreement in relation to this. It is not that they encounter or report the situations less (often it is more frequently), rather it is the fact that the person at home is more able to recognize the extent of the problem.

Although we had found that it was the hearing-impaired person who had first discussed hearing loss at home, we found a greater range of possibilities from the hearing person. For example, more hearing people thought it had been mentioned at work first. Further contradictions occurred in relation to why the doctor was eventually consulted: fifty-five of the hearing-impaired had said it was because of the situations above, but of these twenty-seven of their partners gave different reasons such as pressure from others. When we asked how long it was between first realizing a loss and consulting the GP there were even greater discrepancies, with the hearing person tending to say it was longer. When the hearing-impaired person said it was several weeks only 33 per cent of partners agreed; several months – 50 per cent agreed; at least a year – 19 per cent agreed; and several years – 35 per cent agreed. Most hearing partners knew that the other had gone to the doctor about their hearing loss (92 per cent). When we compare the feelings they recalled of the time of referral to hospital or clinic we find a clear difference of view. While hearing-impaired people felt they were relieved a lot (67 per cent) only 30 per cent of hearing partners agreed and the largest number, 44 per cent, did not see any relief in the hearing-impaired person. In terms of anxiety at referral, 71 per cent of hearing-impaired were at least a little worried while only 53 per cent of hearing partners were worried.

Asking about views of the hearing partner's reaction there was again a wide discrepancy. Hearing-impaired people thought their partners were relieved on referral (83 per cent) while only 48 per cent of hearing people actually were. Forty-five per cent thought their hearing partner was worried but only 31 per cent were.

Few people accompanied their partner to the clinic (less than 30 per cent). Of those who did, there was significant disagreement as to whether allowance was made for the deafness. The hearing-impaired were more positive, 78 per cent thinking people spoke more simply whereas only 26 per cent of partners thought so, and there was specific disagreement in 52 per cent of the cases where the hearing-impaired partner said allowances were made and the hearing disagreed. There were virtually identical findings for speaking clearly and repeating things. Hearing people were much more negative about the allowances made.

There was also some confusion about the reasons given for the deafness (Table 6.12) with perhaps the most interesting being the 10 per cent of hearing partners who thought a hereditary cause had been given. With the more tangible results of the referral, in the issue of a hearing aid we find a greater degree of agreement. Forty-seven per cent of hearing-impaired people felt the aid had helped their hearing a lot as compared to 52 per cent of the hearing partners. Slightly more hearing-impaired people felt it had not helped at all, giving some grounds to the notion that use of the aid is personal and difficulties may not always be discussed. When we asked people specifically about whether they had discussed with their partner about how to adapt to the aid (e.g. how to hold a conversation) 83 per cent of hearing-impaired claimed that they had while only 22 per cent of the hearing partners agreed with this. That is, hearing-impaired people had felt they had communicated but it had not registered with the hearing partner.

Table 6.12   Reasons given for hearing loss at time of diagnosis according to partners (%) (n=97)

	Hearing	Hearing-impaired
No details	31	30
Infection	2	7
Otosclerosis	16	23
Noise	2	5
Meniere's Disease	3	2
Virus	3	–
Accident	3	3
Hereditary	10	3
Mastoid	5	3
Nerve deafness	13	16
Otitis Media	3	5
Pregnancy	–	3
Perforated eardrum	7	–
Hearing is alright	2	–
Total	100	100

Reassuringly, the same percentage of people said a hearing member of the family had tried on the aid. Sadly, they were different people, i.e. thirteen hearing-impaired said others had tried the aid and thirteen hearing said this but of the first thirteen, nine of the hearing partners disagreed, and of the second thirteen, nine of the hearing-impaired partners disagreed. This seems like a fairly fundamental difference of view. There were also some differences in views about how much better situations were after acquiring the aid (Table 6.13). Generally, the hearing partner viewed the aid as much more helpful than did the hearing-impaired person.

CHILDREN

One final area covered in this section concerned the relations with children in the family. There can be problems in dealing with children and we found that most people identified reduction in conversation as the key aspect. A significant proportion (15 per cent) said there were discipline problems as a result of hearing loss although few

Table 6.13 How much improvement was there with an aid in these situations? (% who say 'a lot') (n=97)

	Hearing	Hearing-impaired
Watching TV	52	60
Talking to one other	56	51
Talking to several	48	22
Using the telephone	29	5
Hearing the doorbell	35	8
Talking to callers	33	6
Identifying where sounds come from	29	2

(6 per cent) felt that the children now turned more to their hearing parent. Lack of change seemed to relate quite noticeably to recency with those over two years of recency much more likely to identify changes. Those in the pre-diagnostic group saw less conversation as the effect but the largest group claimed no change.   Comparing the partners in their assessment of how the hearing loss had affected their children we found hearing partners often unaware of the changes experienced by the other. Fifty-seven per cent of hearing people felt there had been no change with the children whereas 71 per cent of the hearing-impaired felt there had been. The commonest problem that parents reported was communication with children. Families reported tackling the practical problems in devising methods of overcoming difficulties in communicating with children. Children themselves sometimes adapted strategies for getting round these difficulties. Irritability resulted from teenage children's lack of concern for their parents' problems in hearing but at the other end of the spectrum babies waking at night caused another set of difficulties. Hearing impaired mothers of young children reported feeling inadequate in the maternity hospital where babies were taken away because they couldn't hear them. Tension between parents arose from the hard-of-hearing parent not hearing babies crying. These topics are discussed further in Chapters 9 and 11.

SUMMARY

This is a complex section to summarize as the findings are extensive. We do find similar patterns to those discovered in our previous work.

Perhaps most worrying are the lengths of time from recognition of hearing loss to presentation at the doctor to seek help. Also worrying is the more negative attitude of hearing-impaired people to deafness and its effects. And there are surprisingly wide discrepancies between hearing and hearing-impaired partners on apparently simple judgements as to whether others tried the hearing aid on and whether coping strategies had been discussed.

There is no 'truth' to be established in these data, only a recognition of differences in perception. We believe self-image is one of the central factors in explaining these, and the extent to which the individual can maintain his or her self-image will determine many attitudes and allow for coping with the stress of hearing loss. These issues will be taken up again later in the book.

7

Dealing with society: employment and social life

It is the outward side of hearing loss that most people see. Despite the temptation to retreat and isolate oneself people still live in a social world governed by economic pressures. The need to work in terms of status and finance is a basic force in western society. The need to meet and deal with others is a necessary part of creating social position. From the home base, the person with hearing loss has to move out. The environment and people who are encountered will greatly affect adjustment.

THE EXPERIENCE OF WORK

I felt dreadful when I had to give up work, it was the most shattering experience I had had because going out to work you felt part of society, you were contributing, you were earning your money. You also had your friends that you went to work with and then suddenly you were cut off, you were in the house alone. Also, of course, financially you were worse off. You were lonely, you felt useless, on the scrap heap, finished. (Campling 1981)

This account of someone with a physical disability giving up work illustrates very well the profound effect of going out to work in terms of self-esteem and independence. Measuring these effects is a difficult task but ensuring that they are taken into account is not.

In this study we asked few questions about work but we did develop the topic in the open-ended interviews we conducted. The principal data reported here come from this latter source. However, we have already examined work in a previous study and can incorporate much of the information here. As in previous studies, we can report that there is no evidence of widespread loss of job because of hearing loss. A few reported job change as a result of hearing loss and two reported loss. Of the people who were in our phase 3 or early phase 4 in our first interviews none had changed jobs between the first and second interviews.

It is fair to say that we have not tackled one of the traditional areas here. That is, we do not offer any solution to the problem of under-employment or unemployment. We found little evidence of job loss but we did find a noticeable level of anxiety about employment prospects. The views of partners are somewhat difficult to incorporate here as they generally had little direct contact with the workplace. It is, never-theless, particularly important from a counselling viewpoint to investigate the work environment and the interaction with people there.

Kyle and Wood (1985) did carry out quite an extensive examination of work attitudes and found that hearing-impaired people tended to have similar dimensions for evaluating their jobs. They tended to be noticeably more satisfied with their job than would hearing people given the job characteristics. When linked to lower promotional possibilities and greater anxiety levels about jobs, we consider this to be evidence of the 'lucky-to-have-a-job' condition. That is, hearing-impaired people, in re-evaluating their position in life, recognize curtailment of opportunity and tend to give up on advancement in their job. Personal interviews indicated awareness of telephone and communication difficulties and the tendency towards not disclosing hearing loss means that hearing-impaired people are inclined to avoid interaction situations where their hearing loss will become apparent. The job environment tends, therefore, to stabilize at a level which the person finds low in stress. Because of this the job becomes highly valued and more satisfaction is attributed to it than it should merit.

Our sample were less unemployed than the general population, i.e. 6 per cent instead of 11 per cent and therefore it is possible that there is a hidden group who have lost their jobs because of hearing loss. However, these are certainly undeclared since we were unable to trace any such people through job centres or the Manpower Services Commission.

Work, as a factor in hearing loss, was reported in a number of different ways. These can be listed as:

1 Direct loss of a job as a result of a hearing loss.
2 The threat of being dismissed following a hearing loss.

3 The strain of constantly trying to hide the extent of a hearing loss in order not to lose promotion or 'credibility at work'.

4 Not seeking work, in particular women with children of school age who say that they would be returning to work but are not looking for work because of their hearing loss and their resulting loss of confidence.

5 Acceptance of lowered expectations of the quality of life at work.
(a) in relationships – for example, a labourer saying 'I don't mind sitting in my car alone eating my sandwiches everyday', because workmates no longer make any effort to talk to him;
(b) in terms of responsibility – justifying a job change to a less demanding job in terms of choice. This may be a positive step but for some it is couched in terms which do not acknowledge the difficulties involved. Examples include moving to maintenance from a foreman's job, and leaving the army;
(c) resulting in 'Hidden' job loss because of hearing problems. For example, the reason given for leaving work by the informant was early retirement following a long period of sick leave for 'depression'. Both of these options, that of leaving work and of taking sick leave, were actually entirely to do with hearing loss. Interestingly, 'hearing loss' was seen as less acceptable than depression by both the respondent and colleagues.

6 Financial strain, loss of a job or lack of promotion, accepting a less well-paid job or not seeking work, all lead to financial strain which affects the others living in the household. How much this is significant obviously depends on the resources of the individual or family to begin with. The increased 'cost' of hearing loss is also reflected in the need for environmental aids, or the need to accompany the person with a hearing loss on journeys they might otherwise have made alone.

Disclosure at work was also a problem area and was linked to promotion. One hard-of-hearing man put his views very clearly: 'I never tell anyone who has rights over me.' Another woman, a teacher, deliberately hid it from her school principal: 'I did try to hide it from her because I didn't want her to think I was weak in any way, but with everyone else I made a big thing about telling them' (48). A civil servant didn't wear his aid to work in case it was noticed. Another man had been told by an army doctor to keep quiet about his hearing loss so as not to lose his chance of promotion and for twelve years they had managed to conceal it on the strength of saying 'I've a cold today, I'm not hearing properly' and similar excuses.

However, being in a more powerful position was worrying too for someone with declining hearing. One man, a foreman, reported: 'I can tell by their faces when I've given them an order that my voice has been too loud, or the wrong tone, and that worries me' (106).

At work anxiety-provoking situations varied according to the type of work. Teachers worried about the noise level rising in the classroom and being unaware of it. Workers on building sites worried about not hearing warning shouts to move out of the way. Shop-assistants were anxious about people asking for things when their backs were turned. For an auxiliary nurse in a mental handicap hospital her worst fears had been confirmed when she had fallen asleep on night duty and not heard the charge nurse approaching her. She was in danger of losing her job. Some people managed well in jobs where speech was not central – one foreman in a printing works said: 'I'm fine, my mates take care of the phone, so it's ok' (103). Another man said: 'My mates cover up for me'.

Work had sometimes been the precipitating factor in seeking help from the services. One woman, a shop-assistant, had been told by her employers to go and get a hearing aid or her job was in jeopardy. A fork-lift truck driver found that his workmates ignored him completely, he sat alone at all breaktimes and in addition one of them had hidden his hearing aid 'as a joke'. He was so outraged at this that he no longer wore it, feeling it 'incensed them', and consequently was even more cut off.

The work situation remains a complex and significant area of the hearing-impaired person's life, which has only been briefly examined here. Just as we have emphasized family as a vital area for study, so also is the work environment if adjustment is to take place. In the case of work problems, it is important to understand that it is not the hearing-impaired person alone who needs to cope but rather there needs to be interactive coping by and with other workmates. The points above indicate that we need to dig much deeper than just an estimate of job loss and consider the quality of working life to a much greater extent. It is not just the driver's hearing aid which is hidden but also the hearing loss itself. While we do not feel there is always a need for self-disclosure we do consider it vital that counselling services in the work setting do attempt to provide others in the work setting with an understanding of hearing loss.

DEALING WITH OTHERS

All our intuitions about hearing loss lead us to expect that social life will be most affected. We conduct the greater part of our interaction through speech and if the capability to receive spoken messages is affected then the interaction is threatened. In the past we have considered that it is the hearing-impaired person who has the loss: loss of sound reception. We could argue that it is the hearing person who has the loss: loss of meaningful message production. Yet in reality it is the *interaction* itself which is affected.

The hearing-impaired person speaks well (even where the loss is total, speaking ability can be preserved) and therefore can contribute significantly to the interaction. The person can initiate interaction and provide relevant information but it may begin to break down as contextual control is lost. It is rather like the person who learns to ask for a particular variety of French bread while in France. The few learned French words work well until the day the baker replies in French – 'we don't have any of that but we've got x, y, z. . . .' and then the person is totally lost. Vocabulary and communication work in only one direction when that language learner is in control. At times this is a useful strategy for people with a hearing loss. 'Start conversations, limit the possible references, try to get others to follow your own topic-setting' is the approach described by Harriet Martineau (1983). Another possibility is to limit the speed of the interaction by checking information given either by repeating what is said or by asking for the information – 'do you mean . . .?' In each case, the strategy helps the individual to retain control of the meaning and thereby allows interaction to take place.

However there are many situations where this level of control is impossible – as soon there are more than two people involved, for example. In any broad, general social interaction where control is difficult hearing loss poses a major threat. Our examination in this section is of these situations. They occur in different contexts: at work, 'in the pub', and also at home. We are therefore concerned with the individual in social interaction rather than simply in social settings external to the home. In the first instance, we will examine how the hearing-impaired person viewed the social interaction and then look at the correspondence between this and other people's perceptions.

Kyle and Wood (1983) asked which situations were difficult for communication. We found mealtimes easy, general conversation easy, and well-defined situations outside easy (buying petrol, talking to the doctor), but 'at home when neighbours or relatives call' was found to be difficult to deal with (76 per cent said it was difficult or very difficult). In this study therefore we asked about strategies for dealing with this social interaction. We asked what people did if they felt left out of conversations when people called at the house (Table 7.1). The results show a quite startling difference between the pre-diagnostic group and the others (chi-square = 19.48, df = 3, p<.001). The former group were much more likely to make it obvious that they wanted to be included, whereas the largest group of those diagnosed were likely to sit and pretend to follow. Since the hearing-loss characteristics of the two groups were similar this constituted a real difference of strategy. One might be surprised in that it seemed to be a maladaptive strategy. There was an additional difference in terms of hearing loss where a significant group of the most deaf took avoidance action by 'starting to do something else'. Those with most hearing tended to be more likely to 'make it obvious'.

Table 7.1 **Strategies used if friends call and you feel left out of the conversation (%) (n=119)**

| | *Pre-diagnostic* | *Diagnosed (yrs)* | | |
		−2	*2–5*	*6+*
Make it obvious that you want to be included	61	26	20	11
Force your way into the conversation	8	19	27	36
Just sit there and pretend you can follow	27	52	47	47
Wait for someone to notice	0	0	3	0
Start doing something else	0	0	3	3
Other	4	3	0	3
Total	100	100	100	100

One might have expected sex differences in this but the differences did not materialize. While 61 per cent of the pre-diagnostic group made it obvious, 17 per cent of males in the diagnosed group did, and 20 per cent of females. In terms of just sitting there, 48 per cent of males *and* females chose this strategy. That is, the difference which arose was due to the difference between the pre-diagnostic and diagnosed groups. There were no differences by job or education level. There did appear to be a tendency for those less deaf to be more likely to 'make it obvious' but the effect of hearing loss was not significant statistically.

Having broken into the conversation, there was then the question of how well others could respond to the needs of the hearing-impaired person. We asked what type of reaction was obtained when they were asked to adapt their conversation. Encouragingly few people reported that others did not understand their request (less than 8 per cent). More of the diagnosed group found people willing to try any new method if it helped them (71 per cent) with the greatest percentage, as one might expect, in those who had had the loss longest (83 per cent). This is a positive finding since virtually no one felt that no real effort was made to include the hearing-impaired person. However, a major difference can be seen among those with more serious losses (>70dB) and those with the mildest losses (21–36dB). In the case of the former only 22 per cent found people willing to try as compared to 83 per cent of the latter. Sympathy and adaptation appear to go to those who need it least or for whom the adaptation is least. There are no systematic differences according to job or education level.

A predicted problem area for people with hearing loss concerns their willingness to participate in social occasions when invited. Often these can be frustrating experiences. We asked for people's views on

Table 7.2   Reasons for refusals of friends' invitations given at least sometimes

	Pre-diagnostic	Diagnosed (yrs)		
		−2	2–5	6+
Because of conversational difficulties	4	44	40	50 (n=117)
Because you're tired of conversation	4	30	33	42 (n=118)
Because they're not sympathetic to your hearing loss	4	26	37	39 (n=117)

this: if they refused an invitation to go round to friends, what was the reason? (Table 7.2)

Again there were marked differences between the pre-diagnostic group and the others. They felt they did not encounter these problems in the same way and did not have the same reasons for cancelling.

There is a further issue and that concerns the way in which the reasons for not going are discussed within the household. If the hearing-impaired person did not go does that mean that the other partner went alone? (Table 7.3)

Table 7.3 Results of discussion of reluctance to go out, solutions at least sometimes (%)

	Pre-diagnostic	Diagnosed (yrs)		
		−2	2–5	6+
We don't go	Situation does not occur	14	28	21 (n=81)
We go, I go reluctantly	"	9	24	27 (n=81)
We discuss it and see if they can help me follow the conversation	"	36	28	30 (n=81)
They go and I stay at home	"	0	4	12 (n=81)
Another compromise	"	14	28	27 (n=81)

The same results appear to follow here. It was those diagnosed as hearing-impaired who had the problems. What we seem to have is an apparent effect of the diagnosis itself or the opposite – people who claim not to have the problem do not present themselves for diagnosis. However, we feel this simple alternative does not completely ring true. Firstly, the members of the pre-diagnostic group did believe they had a hearing loss and had been screened as such. Secondly, as we shall see, their partners did see some of the problems and differed in their views of the strategies used. It seems likely that entering the 'system of hearing loss' may make one more aware of the problems. The labelling of difficulties and the explanation of why these difficulties occur (because of recognized hearing loss) are enough to sensitize the individual and make him or her more problem-oriented.

However, if this were true we would predict that those individuals in the system would have developed positive strategies because of their access to counselling. This did seem the case here (although this cannot be said for the previous questions asked in Table 7.1). The most frequent response was that of discussing the problem and trying to work out a solution which involved participation by the hearing-impaired person. There was a clear hearing-loss effect with more seriously hearing-impaired people finding the situation occurring: i.e. 50 per cent said they didn't go as compared to 15 per cent with mild losses, 67 per cent go reluctantly as compared to 15 per cent with mild losses, and 50 per cent discussed the problem as compared to 13 per cent with mild losses. The more serious the loss the more likely was the situation to occur, but those diagnosed as having the problem saw it as occurring in general much more than the others, irrespective of hearing loss.

HEARING PERSPECTIVES

As participants in social events and as likely collaborators in planned activities the views of people at home are particularly important. We expected that the more similar the views of these partners the more likely was there to be less stress in their dealings with others.

When we made these direct comparisons the first impression was that there was very little agreement concerning the strategies used. Taking the question of being left out of conversations when friends came to the house, we asked which strategy they used. In Table 7.4 we have examined the degree of agreement with the hearing-impaired person's view and the degree of agreement with the hearing person's classification. According to hearing people in the diagnosed group 30 per cent made it obvious that they were left out but only 15 per cent of hearing-impaired people thought they did this.

If we examine Table 7.4 in conjunction with Table 7.1 we can perhaps extract the meaning. For those who were diagnosed as hearing-impaired the only measure of agreement was in the strategy 'just sit there'. But the overall level of agreement was very low. For example, 30 per cent of hearing partners felt that the hearing-impaired made it obvious when they were left out but only 5 per cent of this 30 per cent of hearing-impaired actually realized they made it obvious. Level of agreement among the pre-diagnosis group was higher but their numbers were relatively small in this comparison (n = 15).

When we dealt with responses to this situation we found people thought others were willing to try to help. The same positive finding

Table 7.4   Agreement of hearing and hearing-impaired people in the situation of being left out of conversation (n=75)

Strategy	Overall		% agreement with views of	
	Hearing	Hearing-impaired	hearing	hearing-impaired
Diagnosed				
Make it obvious	30	15	5	10
Force their way into the conversation	12	32	38	14
Just sit there	45	48	55	52
Other	13	5	11	100
Prediagnosis				
Make it obvious	40	67	67	40
Force their way into the conversation	7	0	0	–
Just sit there	53	27	38	75
Other	0	7	–	0

occurred here. The hearing-impaired thought in 77 per cent of the cases that others were willing to try to adapt, and their hearing partners in 82 per cent of the cases. The level of agreement was also high: 81 per cent of the hearing-impaired person's views were supported and 75 per cent of the hearing person's. The hearing people in the pre-diagnostic group were less optimistic with only 54 per cent thinking other people were prepared to try to adapt, but nevertheless agreement was still high.

When asked out to friends those in the pre-diagnostic group felt that others did not try to adapt. However we can see in Table 7.5 that there were problems in deaf and hearing agreeing on the occurrence of these situations.

The level of agreement was low and it seems that the hearing-impaired person refused to go out rather more than was acknowledged by the hearing person. In terms of outcomes of this situation there is

Table 7.5   Reasons for refusals of friends' invitations given at
least sometimes (diagnosed group) (n=74)

	Overall		% agreement with views of	
	Hearing	Hearing-impaired	hearing	hearing-impaired
Because of conversational difficulties	20	47	40	17
Because you're tired of conversation	17	39	46	21
Because they're not sympathetic to your hearing loss	15	35	27	11

primarily agreement in the infrequency of the outcomes. The comparison of the numbers who identified outcomes such as 'we don't go' or 'I go reluctantly' produced very low levels of agreement but the actual numbers in the cells of these comparisons were rather small. It seems therefore that despite some optimistic views on the willingness of others to try to adapt there are still major problems of agreement in identifying the situation which has arisen and in interpreting the strategy which emerges. This is likely to lead to the view we have had expressed frequently in previous projects that people do not completely understand deafness and probably cannot. Hearing-impaired people may not be completely aware of the disapproval they show when they are left out of the conversation but, equally, hearing people seem to be unaware of the extent of the refusals to participate in social life by the hearing-impaired. It is this situation which is most likely to lead to isolation.

   The hard-of-hearing person saw as antisocial strategies such as insisting that people repeat messages and even saying one was having difficulty. One man said: 'It could cause offence if one was too pushy, people might be offended and withdraw friendship or future invites.' Interestingly, being a 'good' guest or companion seemed for this respondent to involve not 'being any trouble', rather like a 'good' child or patient who merits this title by making few demands. There was no expression of his own needs in that situation. For hearing people the comments on social life centred on other people's reactions. Not without insight though, as one wife of a hard-of-hearing man suggested: 'You have to keep asking people to repeat themselves, perhaps they don't like it, I know I get fed up, repeating myself and I'm his wife, so I hate to think what people who aren't connected to him feel.' Another hearing wife said: 'He'll keep on saying to me (when we're out), "What did he say, what did he say?" Well, by the time I've told him what they were saying, I've missed what else was going on ... everybody misses out!' She felt very clearly that she was also involved in the process of any misunderstanding that arose. She was drawn into the process by having to be the one relaying the conversation.

This is something that not everyone sees as their role in situations though. A hearing wife more unusually reported the opposite approach: 'They keep saying, tell him such and such – it's not my place to tell him, I say.'

Social interaction causes embarrassment for the hearing partner as well and sometimes stronger feelings. One hearing wife said: 'It annoys me that he *never* tells people (that he's hard of hearing) ... some people do think he's mental, they don't converse with him.' She reported feeling very let down both by her husband's attitude and that of other people.

We have found in the past a great reluctance to use hearing loss as a strategy in interaction. Very few people would admit to it outside the home, even when communication is seriously impaired. Clearly there is little confidence that others will understand. Unfortunately, as we have pointed out previously (Kyle and Wood, 1983), this ultimately does a disservice to hearing-impaired people since others are not aware of having interacted with a hearing-impaired person and tend to attribute other problems to communication breakdown. The end-product is even less understanding of hard-of-hearing people's needs and capabilities in general.

This is a major problem and we will return to it later in developing the themes of the study. The whole concept of disclosure (i.e. identifying oneself as someone with a hearing loss) is something which we feel must be re-examined in the light of these disagreements about strategy in groups. Hearing-impaired people do tend to be passive and accepting and prefer not to identify themselves even when this creates tension for partners. It is perhaps one of the key areas to be developed for counselling, and might be conceived of along the lines of assertiveness training.

Despite the extent of our data in this field of interaction we are still at a very basic level of understanding. The topic re-emerges in Part III of the book and will then be summarized in the final chapter.

8

Change through hearing loss and over time

The one thing which people who acquire a hearing loss returned to over and over again was the difference that hearing loss made. It is difficult to avoid seeing this major life event in any other way. People spontaneously describe the change hearing loss has made and tend to be very negative. In this chapter we are interested in people's views on the change; in the next we deal with real change in the sense of the temporal change in attitude and belief which we found when we interviewed a second time.

We have already discussed some of the issues and some of our earlier questions inevitably dealt with the change which has occurred. At the same time, change itself does not occur in compartments in the way we have neatly divided our topics: home life, social life and so on. Change occurs throughout daily life as a result of the particular pressures and situations encountered. We tried to ask situation-specific questions as well as more open-ended ones in order to obtain as full a picture as possible. We asked both about personal adjustment and the adjustment of others, and again we were very interested to find the differences between hearing and hearing-impaired people at home.

Perhaps the most obvious question is the simplest to ask: 'How well have you coped with hearing loss?' The vast majority felt they had adjusted reasonably well or very well (over 90 per cent of the diagnosed group and 75 per cent of the pre-diagnostic group). There were no differences according to the recency of onset of loss. The same question about their hearing partner produced an identical response. Over 92 per cent said reasonably well or very well, and 72 per cent of the pre-diagnostic group.

Tackling the change aspect more specifically we asked if hearing loss had affected lifestyle, personality, and happiness (Table 8.1). The unusual pattern of results is not easily explained. The pre-diagnostic group may well be denying change as part of their general positive attitude to hearing loss as we have already seen. At the same time, they may not in reality experience any alteration *because of* this positive compensating attitude and their own life-state. The recency pattern whereby those most recently acquiring a loss are less likely to have felt change is in keeping with the view that the change does not become apparent till later in life. People who have had a hearing loss longest are more likely to have been aware of the change over time. However, it is also possible that change over time has arisen because of age and we have therefore no easy way of disentangling these possibilities.

Table 8.1   **Change as a person since the hearing problem (% saying 'no change at all')**

Change in	Pre-diagnostic	Diagnosed (yrs)			
		−2	2–5	6+	
Lifestyle	93	46	23	33	(n=122)
Personality	82	50	40	33	(n=122)
Happiness	82	46	40	28	(n=122)

There is no doubt that there is a relation with degree of hearing loss since there is a consistent trend by degree of loss in each of these areas. Forty-three per cent of those with the most serious losses (>70dB) feel there has been *a lot* of change in lifestyle, 14 per cent in personality and 43 per cent in happiness as compared to 11 per cent, 0 per cent, and 0 per cent respectively of those with the mildest losses (<36dB).

Although this claimed lack of change is evident in hearing-impaired people it is possible that others see the change. We asked each person to what extent other people viewed them as different as a result of hearing loss. In all cases, the hearing-impaired person felt others were less aware of the change. Whereas 54 per cent of those with recent onsets said their lifestyle and personality had changed, only 21 per cent thought that others saw them differently. This pattern is repeated in each classification. For those with the most severe losses, their perception may be more realistic: although 100 per cent thought lifestyle had changed, 54 per cent thought their personality had cent thought others saw them differently. In mild hearing losses, the results look remarkably similar to those in the recency categories. The pattern of results is the same when we take into account education or social class (job of head of household) and there are no systematic differences in either of these variables. People in lower socio-economic groups are just as likely to recognize changes and understand the views of others. There is therefore a tendency to believe others do not see the change to the same degree. Perhaps it is part of the view that other people never understand.

Considering that this might be situation-specific we asked about the changes in home life, work, and social life. Not everyone was able or prepared to specify changes in addition to the ones already discussed (14 per cent of those diagnosed and 41 per cent of the pre-diagnostic group). However, of those responding the most common responses were that there were conversation difficulties at home (over 70 per cent), at work (over 83 per cent), and in social life (over 77 per cent). Other spontaneous offerings by those interviewed included feeling left out at home and at work, a straightforward decline in social life, and also embarrassment at hearing-aid use. These questionnaire responses seem rather simplified in the light of the general discussions we recorded in the homes. It is likely that the context of the questionnaire offered a framework into which communication problems could be easily placed.

As we have suggested throughout, hearing aids often become the focus of the adaptation required, so we asked people how hearing aids had helped the change. In the first instance we asked about hearing aids and conversation at home. The largest group (48 per cent) claimed that there had been no change in the amount of conversation with their partner at home as a result of hearing-aid use but significantly 39 per cent said conversation had declined. (One extreme view expressed by a hard-of-hearing man was: 'we don't talk much anyway'.) This figure for declining conversation not surprisingly seems directly linked to hearing loss. Those with the mildest loss suffered the least decline in conversation (27 per cent) while 50 per cent of those with the most severe loss said it has declined a little or a lot.

Taking the situation people had claimed to be most difficult (see Chapter 6) we asked what change there had been now. Surprisingly we found no effect of recency – the majority (85 per cent) claimed there was an improvement in dealing with their most troublesome situation and the percentages were almost identical for all classifications of recency. Consistent with previous results it was the most deaf group who saw least change. In fact, 43 per cent felt their hearing aids had given no help or made things worse!

Thinking in terms of others we asked three more questions, two about partners at home and one about hearing loss, aids, and general relationships to others. The first of these dealt with decision-making (Table 8.2). In this context people presented a very optimistic view suggesting that hearing loss was not affecting their decision-making. This would be a very positive finding if it were supported throughout our data but the open-ended interviews suggested rather different results.

Table 8.2   Identifying the effect on decision-making (% agreeing)

	Pre-diagnostic	Diagnosed (yrs)			
		−2	2–5	6+	
It has affected my involvement in decision-making	4	14	11	21	(n=107)
My partner takes most of the initiative	4	0	7	6	(n=107)
I feel I am consulted after a decision is made rather than involved in the actual decision	0	0	0	3	(n=106)
I make more decisions than I used to because I've more time	0	23	63	33	(n=106)
My partner gives way to me more about decisions than previously	0	0	7	6	(n=106)

There was no effect of hearing loss here which is counter-intuitive and is consistent with our supposition that respondents were overrating their involvement.

Dealing with the personal relationship directly we again found most people felt there was little change: 2 per cent felt their relationship had become less personal; 7 per cent said they 'don't chat anymore' at home; 2 per cent felt they had become further apart; 13 per cent felt there was more effort to talk (though this was more likely the longer hearing loss had been present); 17 per cent felt they had been drawn closer together by the hearing loss (again this response was more likely the longer the hearing loss had existed). The response where people acknowledged definite change was in the area of communication becoming 'less trivial' (59 per cent). None of the pre-diagnostic group acknowledged any change in their relationship. The degree of change was slightly greater in those with the more serious losses but not significantly so. Interestingly, those with the most serious losses had the highest percentage both of those who felt they had become closer

Table 8.3 **Comparing the first phase of hearing loss with now (% who agree or strongly agree)**

	Pre-diagnostic	*Diagnosed (yrs)*			
		−2	*2–5*	*6+*	
You consider that you now understand what deafness means and how it affects you personally (e.g. irritability, etc.)	52	75	87	94	(n=115)
You think that you now understand how it affects your dealings with others	42	79	87	97	(n=114)
You feel that you have properly explained to other people at home how to help you	13	75	86	94	(n=112)
You feel that you are under less strain than at first	23	50	37	47	(n=112)
You feel confident to face the future	52	50	50	47	(n=113)

(33 per cent) and those who felt they were further apart (17 per cent) than any of the other categories of hearing loss.

In the final question we asked for judgements about the general personal changes arising because of hearing loss (Table 8.3). Perhaps given the hindsight of all the above results these findings are not so startling. The longer the hearing loss had existed the more likely people were to understand its personal effects and effects on relationships. There was also more chance to explain to others, but more strain and more pessimism about the future.

These items highlight our major predicted differences as hearing loss progresses. There is almost certainly more insight and more realism and more likelihood of discussing this with the others at home. The pattern of results in relation to hearing loss confirms this view that contact increases the adaptation. The most impaired are most similar to those with longest recency of hearing loss, being more aware and more pessimistic.

As before, the primary test of the change in these responses lies in the corroboration by hearing people. In the first area we examined, 'adjustment' to hearing loss, we found the highest degree of agreement. Among hearing partners in the diagnosed group, 89 per cent felt that the hearing-impaired had adjusted well or very well and the agreement with the hearing-impaired person's own view was 91 per cent. Ninety-two per cent of hearing partners felt that they themselves had adjusted 'well' or 'very well' and the agreement with the hearing-impaired was 91 per cent again. For the pre-diagnostic group the results were very similar, with agreement at this high level. Despite the 'apparent' difficulties in family relations both partners independently agreed on their adjustment. However they conceptualized adjustment differently even though they believed it to have taken place. In the area of changes there were some differences. Sixty per cent of hearing-impaired people felt their lifestyle had changed at least a little while only 26 per cent of hearing people agreed. In happiness, 52 per cent of hearing-impaired thought there had been changes but only 34 per cent of partners agreed.

As we found earlier that the hearing-impaired felt that others were less aware of the changes in them as a result of hearing loss, it was interesting to find this confirmed by the hearing partner. Among the hearing-impaired we found 78 per cent claiming that others saw no difference in them as a person while 84 per cent of the hearing partners claimed the same. The picture emerging seemed to be that despite the amount of change, despite the problems occurring, the hearing-impaired person was adjusting sufficiently well for others not to notice.

However, in relation to hearing aids the pattern of agreement was not so great. Although the largest group (49 per cent) felt that their conversation at home was not changed by the use of a hearing aid, a sizeable minority (40 per cent) felt the amount of conversation had declined. This perception was not shared by the hearing group where only 8 per cent felt it had declined and 38 per cent felt that conversation had increased. A tempting proposal is that the hearing people find conversation easier since the hearing aid reduced their communication problem but for the hearing-impaired it simply heightens their sense of isolation by signifying their dependence.

When asked about the situation they found most difficult when they first had a hearing loss the vast majority of hearing-impaired (94 per cent) believed they coped with it better now, but the hearing person was less sure. Only 66 per cent felt that there was an improvement and 24 per cent were not sure. Here hearing partners were rather less positive about the improvement the hearing aid had brought.

In decision-making we found the hearing person consistently less positive about the maintenance of involvement. They believed it had affected the hearing-impaired person's involvement (20 per cent compared to 16 per cent of the hearing-impaired themselves); or that the hearing person took the initiative more (18 compared to 4 per cent); or the hearing-impaired was consulted after decisions were made (16 as compared to 1 per cent); or the hearing-impaired did not try harder to be involved in decisions (100 compared to 61 per cent). The amount of agreement between partners in the pre-diagnostic group was consistently much higher on these points.

There were some differences in the views on personal relations at home. While only 1 per cent of the hearing-impaired group felt their relationship was less personal, 16 per cent of the hearing partners thought it was; 61 per cent of the hearing-impaired thought their communication was less trivial as compared to only 30 per cent of hearing partners; 6 per cent of the hearing-impaired felt that they did not just chat anymore while 27 per cent of their partners agreed to this statement and slightly more of the hearing people felt it had pushed them apart.

In the final question we compared the first phase of hearing loss with the situation now (Table 8.4). The results seem to confirm the

112

views of the hearing-impaired except in one or two notable ways. Although there was generally agreement that they understood the effects of hearing loss on their relationships and understood interaction, it was clear that the hearing-impaired person imagined that the family had been instructed in coping when they had not. Partners (73 per cent) felt that they had not had properly explained to them how to help the hearing-impaired while 87 per cent of the hearing-impaired believed they had explained. Additionally the hearing partner overestimated the adjustment by considering the hearing-impaired person to be under less strain and considering themselves confident to face the future.

Table 8.4   Comparing the first phase of hearing loss with now (% who agree or strongly agree)

	Pre-diagnostic		Diagnosed	
	Hearing	Hearing-impaired	Hearing	Hearing-impaired
Our relationship is less personal	40	33	80	86
Our communication is less trivial	36	14	72	89
We don't just chat any more	8	15	19	87
We make more of an effort to talk to one another than we did before	27	9	61	47
It's drawn us closer together	58	33	75	47

The overall picture then is of a tendency for hearing partners to underestimate the degree of problem of the hearing-impaired, yet at the same time to share the perception that adjustment is taking place. The specific areas of disagreement need to be explored further and in doing this counselling can be more effectively made available.

CHANGE OVER TIME

Given the nature of hearing loss, and the accounts people give us of the creeping isolation it produces, it is not surprising that we expect negative views of hearing-impairment. What began to emerge was a difference in view between our two groups: those who had gone through the state health system for their hearing and those who had not. The small differences in their hearing loss distributions did not adequately explain the relative lack of change experienced by the pre-diagnostic group. It was almost as if they were avoiding a labelling effect, had not accepted the need for diagnosis, and therefore had not undergone the resocialization into disabled community membership which the other majority of our sample had. It is unlikely that the explanation is quite this simple but given the degree of agreement of partners at home it seems clear that there was a whole-family effect which is consistent with 'sick-person-in-the-family' syndrome. In this a re-evaluation of life-style takes place for all family members. This view is more consistent with what seemed to be the case for those in diagnosed groups.

However, we needed to know whether the change they claimed was real and not just an attitudinal shift (although it should be remembered that the term 'real' in this instance applies to an attempt to measure rather than to some actual concrete change). Believing that such a change does occur, and hypothesizing at the outset of our study that this must occur at the beginning of phase 4, we interviewed as many of those in the early stages of hearing-aid use as we were able to. It was not possible to re-interview those in the pre-diagnostic group partly because of our limited resources and partly because their supposed role of control group could not be exploited further without offering them the role of 'disabled'.

Our follow-up study of thirty-two people was therefore an attempt to determine whether their responses to questions had changed over time (ten months on average). On the whole we asked the same questions, with a slightly modified, streamlined questionnaire, and attempted to obtain more open-ended discussion about the changes they had experienced.

As we pointed out in Chapter 5, a significant number changed the date of onset of hearing loss at the second interview, giving grounds to our general assumption that onset for most people is not a fixed point in time but rather a period much as we proposed in Chapter 4.

As a first step we were interested in whether rated hearing loss had changed. We asked them to complete the same 8-point rating scale (the Gallaudet scale). There were some discrepancies but the slight movement was towards better hearing since the first interview and for

114

most people since about the time of hearing-aid issue. When respondents were asked about hearing without an aid after the ten-month gap between interviews, 41 per cent felt their hearing had improved, 37 per cent said it was the same and 22 per cent said it was worse (n=32).

On the first occasion there had been little contact with materials on information on deafness. We found very little change. One person had read a leaflet, none had gone to lip-reading classes, none had joined a club or group for hearing loss but four more had seen a television programme for deaf people. It appears that our interviewing had no effect on action in this sphere even if we suppose that it heightened awareness.

We did not repeat questions about the early stages of hearing-aid use and the situations which were drawn from phase 2 and 3 since so few people had newly-acquired aids. The main concern was with attitudes and the perceived changes in personal and social life.

In terms of stated attitude to hearing loss people tended to have become more negative. People seldom tried to ensure that the hearing-impaired followed what was said (41 per cent in interview 2, only 9 per cent in interview 1). The family adjusted their social lives to help (38 per cent as opposed to 63 per cent before). Hearing-impaired people were more irritable because of stress (66 per cent as opposed to 28 per cent before). Hearing loss meant that social life could not continue in the same way (28 per cent as opposed to 13 per cent before). The pattern suggests greater experience producing more negative feelings for these people. We asked again about their experiences at the clinic and how they were told and these generally followed the same pattern as previously reported. This gives some validity to the previous claims. When we asked about the 'label',. i.e. how they viewed themselves as 'deaf', 'hard-of-hearing' etc. we found some changes in view although 'slightly hard of hearing' remained the most popular.

One question added in these second interviews concerned the use of 'drugs' in the previous year. This produced a surprisingly high incidence of the use of sleeping tablets (15 per cent) and tranquillizers (15 per cent) but less use of anti-depressants (3 per cent), compared with 10 per cent of the population of the UK.

We dealt with the question of interaction in a number of situations which highlighted the differences in the diagnosed group. In the situation where the hearing-impaired looked for change in others we found a remarkable number had become more pessimistic about change (Table 8.5). The change from 84 per cent who previously

Table 8.5   Requests to people to adapt their conversation produce the following responses (%)

	Willing to try	*Don't understand No effort*
In interview 1 they said:	84	16
In interview 2 they said:	45	55
Those who said 'Willing to try' in interview 1, in interview 2 said:	46	54
Those who said 'Don't understand/ No effort' in interview 1, in interview 2 said:	40	60

claimed others were willing to try to only 45 per cent in the second interview was a significant switch. Over half of those who initially were positive by the second interview believed people were less helpful.

Overall, we did confirm that changes were towards more negative views. Whereas on the first occasion people were seen to be willing to try to adapt (58 per cent) by the second interview this had dropped to 26 per cent. Of those who had felt there had been no change in lifestyle because of hearing loss (34 per cent), 64 per cent had now decided there was a change in lifestyle. The same pattern occurred in person-ality and happiness. There were increases in the number of people who saw the hearing-impaired as different.

However, at the same time, this was part of the learning process and more people had better insight. On the first occasion 10 per cent felt they understood about deafness, but by the second this had risen to 61 per cent, and 55 per cent (as opposed to 7 per cent earlier) understood how it affected others. There was more confidence to face the future.

What comes out clearly from all the analysis of these second interviews is the amendment downwards of the expectations of individuals, the increasingly negative view of the circumstances in which they find themselves, and the tendency to relinquish control of areas such as decision-making. We will require further analysis of this data to provide a more detailed account, but obviously there is a need for counselling

116

intervention with these groups of people in this early part of phase 4 of our model. The changes occurring are largely changes which we would not wish and are probably predictable from our limited counselling services.

Change occurs in both people's perception of it and also in real terms when followed longitudinally. The change is dynamic and inter-active in the sense that it takes shape from the interacting factors at home and at work. But the change may not be useful adjustment if it is all in the negative direction we seem to see here. On the one hand change beyond diagnosis creates more negative realism, while on the other hand, avoidance of diagnosis (pre-diagnostic group) offers better joint insight in the family and slightly more positive responses over-all. We believe these results highlight weaknesses in our support services but indicate the point of entry in future: the family and their interaction.

THE EXPERIENCE OF HEARING LOSS

Making sense of hearing loss

'When you're totally deaf, there's that hushness, like when you wake up in the morning and it's been snowing and there's two feet of snow outside there's that deathly hush' (71). This man was describing graphically what it feels like to suffer a complete loss of hearing, although in fact he was describing something which for him was only temporary. This chapter looks at people's descriptions of living with a hearing loss – what they actually say about the process. It examines the nature and quality of the experience of hearing loss both from the point of view of those who experience it and those who are closest to them. How people experience a particular disability is affected at least as much by what they believe about it as by the underlying organic features of the condition.

As discussed in Chapter 3, there is some point in using the theories of illness behaviour to examine coping strategies used for an acquired hearing loss. Although, ideally, hearing loss should not be defined in medical terms alone, the resources and context of hearing impairment at present are firmly linked within the health service. The sense that people make of hearing loss very often starts with diagnosis given by doctors. Lay knowledge about hearing loss is included within this theory as part of the information that people bring to what is happening to them.

Here we are talking of people who at some point use their lay knowledge of hearing loss to decide whether or not to consult a doctor (in some cases it was a traumatic loss which occurred as a result of an accident so those people did not directly consult). This group had some notion of what was unacceptable in their view. The case for looking at hearing loss in terms of illness behaviour is reinforced in conditions where other 'symptoms' existed such as discharge from the ears, vertigo, lack of balance, or repeated ear infections. For these people there is a clear case for looking at adjustment to hearing loss in terms of 'illness action', i.e. consulting a medical practitioner. For most people, the doctor is the person to consult about a hearing loss. There are those others who obtain a private hearing aid with no medical consultation who do not define it in this way.

In the pre-diagnostic sample, people opted for a non-illness or disability model for their hearing loss. They selected repeated syringing of the ears to deal with their hearing loss. Even though this is a 'medical' solution it could be or was perceived as a 'non-medical' option by the users because it is often administered by the 'works nurse'. Such an occupational health nurse was often not seen as a part of the central health services. All those interviewed had to decide, at some point, whether or not there was something wrong with their hearing and whether to consult a doctor. From there, the choice was to follow a route through ENT, to the acceptance of the diagnosis of hearing loss with or without the offer of a hearing aid or surgery. It may therefore be argued for using illness behaviour as a model for the collection of data in this field.

Goffman's (1963) work on stigma, discussed in Chapter 3, and the relevant theory, will be used throughout this chapter. In the open-ended section of the interview people were however asked how they felt about their hearing loss (or that of those they lived with). This chapter examines qualitative data collected in this part of the interview. The emphasis will be on understanding informants' views of their situation and the sense they make of their position. There are at times apparent or logical inconsistencies in their accounts. The questions addressed were:

1 What does it feel like to have a hearing loss as an adult (or live with someone who has)?
2 How is the label 'hard-of-hearing' or 'deaf' construed by the individual affected and by their immediate group?

Because of the large number of informants, rather than repeat details, code numbers are given for each interview so that they can be looked up in the list of informants given in Appendix 3. This impersonality is not meant as a sign of disrespect but merely as an easy way of cross-referencing.

WHAT IT FEELS LIKE TO HAVE A HEARING LOSS

What do the ways in which people describe their hearing loss tell us about their attitudes towards it and about the nature of that experience? Describing what it feels like to lose your hearing a 45-year-old woman teacher said: 'You know when you walk into a soundproof room it's like walking into cotton wool – that's just what it's like' (48). The same woman spoke about what happened when the batteries ran out in her two hearing aids:

> The panic does set in because you can't hear, it's a very claustrophobic feeling because it's a dead-end feeling probably because I don't let the situation exist for long therefore for me it's a sudden cutting off of all contact. I can't hear cars going by, I can't hear my own voice, can't hear things ticking or bumping. (48)

The first of these descriptions is almost a comforting one, and like the earlier description of a snowy landscape, presents a recognizable description. The second however introduces a sense of isolation and discomfort. It agrees with Ramsdell's (1962) claims about different levels of hearing – being aware of things outside on a different level from those close to hand. This sense of isolation is more common than comfort in the accounts given by the people interviewed. Explaining what it felt like to suffer a hearing loss people used words which included describing feeling 'at a loss', 'in a tunnel', 'out of action', 'a dead-end feeling', 'cut off'. Words that described an unpleasant sense of being isolated and being prevented from joining in the hearing world were used in this context. There is a difference in talking about the 'natural silence' of being hearing-impaired and the contrasting silence of wearing a hearing aid and taking it out. The words above applied mostly to people who were describing what it felt like when hearing aids had broken down or the batteries had run out. Having a hearing aid is often part of the experience of having a hearing loss and it may heighten the sense of being cut-off when it is not being used.

A very different view was expressed by a woman explaining her problem with a hearing aid:

> It's too agitating, too much bother, I'd rather be in my own little world. Look, I'm happy in my own little world, it's a quiet world and it's lovely. I don't hear all my neighbours or people shouting or anything like that. It is just beautiful – I love this world. See, so I don't really want a hearing aid for that as well. (83)

For her, the peace and quiet was something to be valued. (When asked if her husband was part of this world too, she replied that he was when he was there, which wasn't often.) This is the complete opposite of a woman who described as 'terrible, awful' (30) the effect of having no hearing aid or no possibility of using one or of another man who talked of feeling 'devastated' and being in 'dead trouble' if it went wrong permanently (94). It also contrasts with the man saying 'the aid is my only contact with the world' (39).

All these descriptions of hearing loss vary considerably, and what some people describe as an appalling prospect others see as desirable. Silence is preferred by the woman who chose not to wear her hearing aid rather than suffer the assortment of noises amplified by the aid. It is a constant complaint of hearing-aid users that the aid amplifies the rustling of crisp packets or the clattering of washing up and that there is a lack of understanding about this by hearing people as well as sometimes a lack of explanation from audiological technicians about how difficult it will be to get used to. The 'hush' and 'quiet world' type of descriptions apply obviously only to those people who do not experience tinnitus (discussed on p. 87). Some people opt for the disadvantages of no aid rather than what they see as the disadvantages of wearing a hearing aid. Choosing a hearing aid may cause the silence to be more noticeable.

A hearing partner talked about the contrast between using a hearing aid and not wearing it:

> It's much more of a contrast after a hearing aid – if you go deaf gradually you're not aware of how things sort of diminish but if you've got a hearing aid and suddenly it's switched off and then there's silence, something's wrong and you're frightened of what you ought to be hearing or might be missing. (48)

Her hard-of-hearing partner said to this comment: 'You couldn't have said that two years ago could you, that's not the kind of insight anyone else has.' She admired the change in perception towards greater understanding. The stark contrast between wearing or not wearing an aid was one reported by other hard-of-hearing people. A hearing person (48) described above what she thought it felt like not to hear properly and her partner recognized the insight and approved of it. This shared perception is unusual. Most of the informants felt very strongly that a hearing person could not know 'what it feels like'.

'You've got to be deaf yourself to understand', was the common theme. One exception was the hearing impaired woman who said: 'My husband understands my deafness better than I do' (27). She deferred to him throughout the joint interview, and while being interviewed individually made a point of coming to her husband (who was being interviewed in the same room) to ask if she would hear better if she moved into another room with the interviewer. She did not seem at all confident of her own ability to judge her own hearing and in fact lacked confidence about other areas of her life. Her belief stated here was that her husband knew what was best for her in practical terms. However, this was not necessarily recognizing that he knew what it felt like to have a hearing loss as the earlier couple were saying. Many more accounts were given of hearing people 'understanding the problems' or 'trying to help' rather than actually empathizing with what was happening to the hard-of-hearing partner. The marked reluctance to try on hearing aids, discussed in Chapter 6, and thus 'experience' something of what was happening, is a sign of this general lack of empathy.

A woman in her 30s spoke of trying to explain to her husband some of the difficulties she was experiencing:

> He wasn't very patient at first, he was very impatient, wouldn't repeat himself at all. I used to say 'pardon', 'Oh God, it doesn't matter', and then I used to get upset and he would say 'I'm sorry' and I said 'you just don't realize what it's like for me' and I explained and he realized then it must be awful to be in our [people with a hearing loss] situation, now he's more helpful. (89)

Hearing-impaired informants rarely talked of 'how it felt' to their hearing partners but did talk about communication problems. This woman (89) actually explained her problems in communicating by constantly asking for repetition – not understanding what was said rather than explaining to her husband how withdrawn she felt.

Tinnitus is another facet of this experience which is equally difficult to explain to people who do not suffer from it. The same problem arises with trying to talk about the phenomenon of how a hearing aid amplifies every sound, not just the voice. This means that just as someone shouting can hurt the ears of hearing-aid users, so can a motorbike going by in the background. These two aspects of hearing impairment were reported as very difficult to convey to hearing people in a way that was sympathetically received.

This section has looked at how people have described what it feels like to have a hearing impairment. This includes what it feels like to experience that change in the level of hearing caused by wearing a hearing aid. The basic experience was described in interview according to the way people saw their disability. More people saw it as a threatening loss of contact with the world than as a soothing release from the noise and bustle of the world. The other topic raised was communicating what the hearing impairment felt like to people who were hearing. Explaining what 'not being able to hear properly' was like or the effects of wearing a hearing aid was not felt to be easy. It proved to be difficult and, as our study showed, was not particularly well understood by hearing people.

SELF-IMAGE

When people talked about how hearing loss had affected their view of themselves very different words were used: 'You're a different person, you're not so cocky' (26) was how one woman saw herself after suffering a perforated eardrum and then a hearing loss. Her family supported this, saying she no longer controlled them in the same way as she had done before.

Other people, however, saw themselves as remaining just the same as they were before the hearing loss, emphasizing that basically they were the same people inside. A journalist said of his own sudden hearing loss:

> You have to take into consideration one's personality. I'm lucky because I'm a sensible intelligent sort of chap. I have managed to overcome this problem, I've thought about it, I'm surrounded by people who are intelligent, who put up with me – now if I was not an intelligent man, if I didn't actually enjoy reading *The Times* and doing the crossword, which will keep me going for hours, what the hell would I do then? I can still quite enjoy music, even if I can't hear it – I can read, I can see and, much more important and inside there [points to head], I can hear. (94)

He hung on to his individuality and sense of self as a way of overcoming his hearing loss – he prized his 'intelligence' and put his success in dealing with his disability down to that. This could be seen as a denial of his problem and therefore as one coping mechanism. He had experienced considerable difficulty as a result of his hearing loss. He had been forced to leave a job he was very fond of and to miss out on music. He complained of both at different points in the interview, yet did not include them in his intelligent response.

126

Another man, a bookseller, talked of similar feelings but in terms of socio-economic position rather than intelligence. At first he said, talking of adaptation to hearing loss, 'It depends entirely on the individual', but then that 'socio-economic position' had a lot to do with how people adapted. He had previously said he'd adapted because of his interests:

> This sounds terribly patronizing but let's say the straightforward casual labourer who has no interests, no culture beyond wanting to finish his work, go home, eat a meal and go out to the pub. He is going to face a totally different set of problems because he is likely to associate with people on a similar cultural level and who are probably going to jeer and deride his hearing loss, because I believe I am correct in saying that disabilities are looked upon less compassionately the lower you go down the socio-economic scale. (58)

This informant saw himself, rather like the earlier man, as overcoming his problems because of what he was before the hearing loss. He had a very rigid view of how society operated and again was unwilling to admit to his difficulties. Both saw themselves as unchanged by the loss and both had a strong sense of self which seemed undiminished by the change in their hearing. This may not have been a realistic assessment of either man's position. They both felt confident enough to expect other people to adapt to their needs (in their own families especially). Interestingly, they both felt they had 'coped' because of what they had achieved before it happened to them: 'Let's face it', one of them said, 'I started ten years ahead' (94).

Although these two men may be operating defence mechanisms here, by avoiding difficult situations for example, their accounts raise an interesting issue about self-esteem. They suggest that if people start off from a point of low self-esteem and little confidence, they have an additional 'handicap' as the two informants above would imply. They felt their intelligence and social-class position helped them to cope or at least avoid difficult situations. This would imply that people in more powerful positions adapt better (or make those around adapt to them!) Admittedly, if you can pay for a lip-speaker or a Palintype operator, you can automatically command a better position for yourself in the workplace. People are less willing to put themselves out for a student who cannot follow a lecture, for example, than for a GP who has problems with his hearing. A person working on a noisy building site as an unskilled labourer may certainly have more difficulty in a job where he cannot assemble resources to back himself up or sufficient authority to make people be patient with his hearing problems. There is a great deal here to be explored, how education (rather than intelligence), power, and financial support can alter the course of a hearing loss. Race, gender, and social class, as well as age, must all play a significant role here.

FINDING OUT WHAT'S WRONG

The way in which a hearing loss (or any illness or disability) is interpreted by the person is obviously influenced by the manner in which the news is given. Some people feel they have received no proper explanation and are therefore confused, others feel very clear about what is wrong with them and that they therefore know exactly what to expect, or felt nothing was wrong so acted accordingly.

Because hearing loss is such a gradual process there is often a gradual dawning of realization that something is wrong. People very often take a long time to accept that there is anything wrong, if ever. The pre-diagnostic sample demonstrated this very clearly. Several of the men admitted they could not hear the telephone or door bell, or spoke on the phone and missed a great deal of conversation yet felt that 'there was nothing wrong'. They justified it in terms of wax in the ears or 'a cold' or 'just the way I am'. Seeking help was often a process initiated by hearing partners. Other symptons such as ear infections which caused pain or discomfort sometimes precipitated a visit to the general practitioner.

The hearing loss of some of our informants was the result of an accident or failure of an operation, so it was a sudden and traumatic loss. Sudden loss occurred in one man's case following a brain tumour. An eardrum perforated whilst swimming had caused one informant to have a dramatic hearing loss. Four people had road traffic accidents resulting in a sudden hearing loss and two men had experienced the same thing after having heart attacks. Five people had suffered a marked decline in hearing after an operation which had failed. One woman blamed her loss on drugs given to her for tubercolosis twenty years earlier. Another felt hers was shock following the death of her mother in a fire. One man blamed his on an accident at judo and another man felt his was due to a wall falling on him (both had these explanations given by doctors). One woman blamed her hearing loss on the fact that her father used repeatedly to hit her about the head when she was a teenager. A doctor had told her this was why, when she was in her early 20s, but since then she said she had never mentioned it when she'd been to see any other doctor because she felt ashamed. Three women had suffered their hearing loss after childbirth. One of these had lost her husband when her second baby was only a few weeks old and her hearing had decreased significantly then. The effects of sudden trauma on hearing is an area which is much neglected. Several informants referred to the fact that their hearing became worse when they experienced stress. Five people in the group who had contact with the audiological services said their hearing loss was due to noise at work; two worked in printing shops, one in a tobacco factory, one was a welder, and one a lorry driver. Many more worked in noisy environments but did not mention the possibility of that as a causal factor. However, fifteen of the pre-diagnostic group put their hearing problems down to a noisy workplace – mainly in the aerospace and printing industries. (These fifteen were the only ones again who made the connection.) Two men in this sample had suffered hearing damage during the war, one from a bomb blast and one from gunfire. In the audiology services group one man had suffered a hearing loss from a bomb blast during his time in the army.

The experience of a *sudden* loss was not common to all these groups, and work-related hearing loss, for example, was a gradual process. Hearing loss after childbirth sometimes improved temporarily. A very gradual decline in hearing is completely different to a sudden dramatic loss but the nature of the cause and the explanations given may be even more important for working out ways of coping, and, as the examples above show, a range of factors can cause acquired hearing loss. For the majority of our informants, discovery of the loss was a gradual process in itself. One woman in her 30s who had a deaf father and grandfather gave a typical description:

> I only noticed because my husband pointed it out. He said 'when you're in bed and you're laid on your good side you don't hear what I'm saying'. I said 'Don't talk rubbish, of course I do.' I wouldn't believe it, I didn't want to believe, then I put it down to a cold, the doctor thought it was catarrh, then the specialist said it was otosclerosis. (89)

Her reluctance to accept any suggestion that she wasn't hearing properly is very common. It must be difficult to assess when you have only your own hearing to compare with – we never really have any sense of what other people are hearing in a situation. Going to the specialist is seen as *legitimization* for many people. It represents a clear label for what is wrong and an indication that something needs to be done. In a family with six children, there was a lot of trouble with a seventeen year old who was irritable about his father's hearing. The mother said:

> I think if you [the father] said to him – 'right now – I've been to the hospital. I'm definitely going deaf in this ear, it's going to be worse' – then he would be different altogether. You'd find that irritableness would go. As it is, when you say 'you're talking on my deaf side' that's more an expression than a fact to him. (34)

This woman felt that a 'proper' diagnosis would make his son change his behaviour towards his father. She was seeking some legitimization of the father's problems. The husband, a lorry driver, however, firmly refused to accept any label of hearing loss at the hospital visit (or the hearing aid that was offered). He said he was 'fine, not deaf' and 'I just got to ask them to repeat things that's all' (34). He did not see this as connected with hearing loss, just part of normal behaviour even though he talked of having a 'deaf side'. He had rejected the diagnosis and assistance offered by the hospital.

Comments made about the diagnosis given in hospital varied from: 'No medical details, I think it might be connected with the second baby, I didn't understand and he seemed too busy to ask him to repeat it' (6); to a very clear, concise explanation: 'Bilateral acoustic neuroma, fully explained and understood' (40).

The way the diagnosis was given was obviously important. One couple both felt very let down by their consultant's approach: the consultant had said to the husband 'you're deaf', the man looked at him, he wrote it down, the patient said 'what, for life?' and the consultant wrote 'yes'. The wife said afterwards 'and that was that – nothing'. This couple had had considerable trouble following this poorly delivered diagnosis. They felt badly let down by the health service and felt that nothing was done to help them, that they were left to struggle on alone.

RESPONSE

How people responded to diagnosis varied. One man described the effect of the diagnosis as being 'a feeling that from now on it's a question of coping with life rather than living it'. Another hard-of-hearing woman said:

> I could have quite happily strung myself up when I first went deaf. If I'd had the courage I would have. I couldn't see that I was going to be any sort of mother to them, I couldn't understand them. Something that really brought it home to me happened – I was sitting here, we'd had breakfast ... [one child fell down the stairs and came in crying with his nose bleeding] I'd not heard and he'd had to pick himself up to come and tell me. (64)

It was an accident with her child which really brought home to this woman what it meant to have a hearing loss. Her horror was to do with feeling she would be a poor mother. Her initial reaction was one of extreme depression, but by the time of the interview she felt she was coping well.

Responses to diagnosis came from the hearing partners as well. One woman said of her husband's diagnosis: 'I felt so sorry for him, nothing you could do to help. At night he put the alarm to his ear, closer and closer, nothing at all, he was very down' (46). Another said of her husband: 'I was quite sad, couldn't believe it, I felt something could have been done. Bill doesn't groan or moan though, he lives with it' (63). Both women felt helpless to do anything and did not feel their husbands had received enough help from the hospital.

Depression was reported by some people but noticeably more often by those whose hearing had improved since, either because of an operation or an amelioration of their loss. These retrospective accounts of hearing loss semed to paint a bleaker picture which may have been a more honest picture because the respondent was no longer in that situation. There is obviously a vested interest in making the best of a circumstance (especially in an interview). One mother and 28-year-old daughter talked about their response on the first hospital visit to finding out about the daughter's hearing loss. The mother said: 'I felt awful, she's such a good girl, I couldn't bear to think of anything hurting her. She said to me "why should it be me, I haven't done anything wrong?"' The daughter agreed: 'That was how I felt at first. ... I was glad when I knew there was a lot of other people with it, not glad but I thought I was the only one with something wrong with me and when you realize that there are people worse off then you don't feel so bad about it' (33).

Her reaction was mixed with anger at the 'unfairness' of it because she was so young, hearing loss was something she associated with ageing. Her reaction to diagnosis was not noticeably changed by her contact with the hospital services but she did not express quite so negative a view as another deafened man of his future and the hospital visits. 'What's the point, I'm deaf for life, why should I go, sit around a hospital for an hour, see a man for two minutes, it's not going to make any difference' (1). His view of coping did not include hospital as a resource but he felt life had dealt him a double blow as his hearing loss followed a period of unemployment. Very few people mentioned outside resources as a help to adjusting to their hearing loss, feeling it was very much left to themselves. One woman described getting over her own reaction to losing her hearing. At first she found she was withdrawing more and more from everyone.

> I got myself out of it, you know by really realizing 'what am I doing to myself?' – I mean, no one else is doing it, it's you. That's done it if you're going to sit back and let yourself do it, there's nothing anyone else can do ... you need someone to lean on occasionally, I'm not saying you don't, but basically you've really got to get to grips with it and think well this situation's not going to get any better, in fact, it will probably get worse, so if you can't cope with it now you'll never be able to cope. (89)

She obviously saw it as something that was up to her and she did not expect any outside help except in the short term. Her response was painful and it took several years for her to feel she'd 'adjusted'.

In contrast another couple agreed that they both felt relatively unconcerned about the discovery of the husband's hearing loss: 'You just accept it as a fact, oh well, he can't hear and that's that, there's nothing you can do about it' (69). They experienced none of the feelings of it being 'the end of the world' or of being 'a misfit' that the previous woman had gone through. What emerges though is that the way hearing loss is presented initially is very important; explanations, some idea of what might happen, and some practical advice do seem to affect the response to diagnosis.

Seeking help and going through the system, being labelled as hard-of-hearing or deafened, means making some changes both for those labelled and for the people they live with. Some response is required to being given a label like this, some sense has to be made of it. The process of seeking help and receiving a diagnosis involves them all.

HOPING FOR A CURE

One aspect of being diagnosed was the personal definition and its context. Hearing loss as a disability was accepted by some informants. But there were gradations of acceptance. Some people who adopted the 'ignore it, it will go away' approach felt it certainly was not a permanent state. For others this interpretation was in fact correct, because they did recover some degree of their hearing either by operation or by improvement in their condition. Some notably improved their ability to hear by the use of a hearing aid. Some informants felt there was no point in adjusting to a hearing loss as a cure would be found. Others felt just as strongly that this was a negative approach. One man in his 40s summed up this latter approach.

> I don't know enough about research but I certainly don't expect to be cured. ... I should be delighted if there was one, but I don't expect it. I wouldn't advise people to think in terms of a cure, rather in terms of adapting to the hearing loss they've got. (58)

He felt he had to get on with living as he was, rather than building up false hopes of a cure. This is echoed by a girl in her early 20s who had been depressed and taken anti-depressants after suffering a hearing loss at 21 years of age: 'Well I think I've just accepted it now, you've got to accept, there's nothing you can do about it, there's no cure for it, is there?' (33)

She had reached this point of resignation only after a very difficult period during which she had felt it was very unfair that it had happened to her when she was so young, but shared the view of the hopelessness of waiting for a cure. Some people feared 'a cure' in the sense that they were afraid to undergo an operation where a risk of further hearing loss was involved. One man in the pre-diagnosis sample had been to the hospital once and had not returned because of 'fear of the knife', after the consultant had mentioned that an operation might be possible. Other people expressed the desire to 'hang on to what I've got' and did not therefore wish to take the risk of further hearing loss rather than fearing the operation itself.

Hope of a cure was however expressed by some other informants. A woman in her 30s said: 'To have normal hearing I'd give anything *anything* in this world to have it put right', but she then went on to say 'I know there's an operation but it's so risky ... there's a chance it would go completely and I don't want to take that chance' (30:2). So although this informant desperately wanted to be 'cured' she did not feel able to risk the hearing that she still had. Her hope for a cure was very much tied up with fearing the future.

> If I sat down and thought about it I would get depressed. Every day it's one of those things I cannot block out of my mind. Whether I'm going to go deaf, whether it's going to get worse. Nobody knows what the future is going to hold, but you've got to get on with your life. You've got to cope until they come up with something that might help. (30:2)

She was still hoping that something would turn up – at the same time acknowledging that life had to carry on – but was still finding life 'a struggle' at the second interview. Her fear of the future was very vivid to her as she found the present situation quite difficult enough to cope with. She talked of committing suicide if she were to go 'stone deaf'. Her hope for a cure, though, did not extend to risking the gloomy future she foresaw if her hearing got any worse. This was in spite of admitting that her husband would be far less embarrassed by having a hearing-impaired wife than she was to be that wife.

Another group of informants talked very positively about hoping for research to improve their chances of regaining their hearing. One man, a labourer in his late 30s who wore two hearing aids and had a severe hearing loss, said 'I hope they get techniques a lot better and *put my hearing back*' (67:2). He had a very simple view of what he wanted from science and technology. At the same time he seemed to make very little fuss of his very marked hearing loss. He showed little concern for any problems he might have and expressed himself very content with his life. He made light of what must have been a considerable amount of effort involved in communication.

The most extreme case of hoping for a cure was a woman profoundly deafened in her 20s. She was 'putting all' her hopes on a cochlear implant and was confident that this would restore her to normal hearing. She did not want to learn sign language which she saw as 'giving in to deafness' and definitely saw the whole of her life as a battle both with hearing loss and with other insensitive hearing people: 'You've not got to let it [deafness] beat you' (64). Her main advice to other hearing-impaired people was 'Don't let the sods get you down!' (64) [meaning hearing people who were not helpful]. She had already coped with the death of her husband when he was only 23 leaving her with two very young children, and had been a single parent for nine years. She appeared resolutely cheerful in both interviews at the same time as being very realistic about her life. She was however determined not to identify with other hearing-impaired people (especially not people born deaf) and had not had any communication training of any sort. She would not contemplate the future as a deafened person as she was so convinced that a cochlear implant would solve all her problems.

Hoping for a cure then was sometimes seen as a waste of time preventing people from adapting and sometimes as the only way to cope with an intolerable present. Beliefs about the inevitability of increasing (or continuing) hearing loss were obviously influenced by the hope that a cure might turn up. Surgery was not seen as an unqualified blessing as many people feared the consequences. It was also not the only cure mentioned. Informants had tried acupuncture, allergy diets, homeopathy, and yoga, and one man said he had improved greatly as a response to faith-healing. Some of these were not seen as 'cures' as such but rather as amelioration of the symptoms. Many people expressed disappointment with a hearing aid, which they (and their families) had often wrongly perceived as a 'cure' for deafness. They were disillusioned by the reality of hearing aid use. The stage of waiting for a cure seems to be a key aspect of the whole process and a time when adjustment may be delayed. This needs to be taken into account when hearing-impaired people are being counselled.

IMAGES OF DISABILITY

Do people who suffer a hearing loss see themselves as disabled, or merely as having an inconvenience in their lives? Does finding out what's wrong make any difference?

Acquired hearing loss is most commonly a gradual process and this does seem to have some bearing on how it is viewed. In terms of disability, 'deafness' was frequently compared to 'blindness' by both groups of informants, in terms of a 'which is the worst' comparison and the difference in public sympathy towards them. How the hearing loss was seen by hearing and non-hearing informants obviously played an important part in how they responded to it. Definitions of the hearing impairment ranged from hardly acknowledging it was there to seeing it as a basic handicap.

One couple who admitted that they had had arguments because of the husband's declining hearing said that they saw it in the following way. The wife (B) began: B: 'I don't think we really treat it as a handicap, not really, just a bit of a nuisance.' A: 'That's all it is, really.' B: 'And we treat it as more or less that it might go away – it's not going to, but you do' (66).

In spite of saying it was 'just a bit of a nuisance', they had previously said that it had changed their 'whole life from the point of view of communication' and the wife said she had 'given up' on conversation: 'You have to pick what you want to say, if it's important enough and I'm afraid you've got to leave the rest.' They both admitted it was 'wrong' to be the way they were and that they should both 'try more'. Thinking of hearing loss as a nuisance may have contributed to finding it difficult to cope with. Since they (a) did not see it as a handicap and (b) behaved as though it would go away, they had not really come to terms with it. At the same time, however, they recognized it as having changed the whole of their lives in terms of communication. Would seeing hearing-loss as a 'disability' have made any difference to them? Would they have coped better or 'tried more' as they described it?

Unchanged behaviour is echoed in another set of accounts. A couple talked about their approach to the husband's hearing loss which occurred after a car accident. The wife, a veterinary student, said

> I think the reason I make sure it's not a problem is that I wouldn't like to accept there is a problem, so I always go the other way. I refuse to accept that Brian is disabled. His limp is all right, because to me that's not in any way a handicap but because I wouldn't like it [hearing loss] to happen to me, I don't really want it to happen to Brian so if I ignore it, it goes away. (47)

Her husband agreed, recognizing that her attitude influenced his own. He continued straight on from her comment:

> That is very, very true in actual fact, I think eyes and hearing are the two things that would make one sort of – oh dear, that's not going to happen to me – and I think Janet feels if she doesn't take any notice and just treats me normally, it will go away, it's not there, it's not a problem. But I don't accept that I've got a problem, I try to forget it, when I'm out, I know I've got a hearing aid, but I don't think 'oh good Lord!' The tinnitus is there, and that's it. (47)

Fortunately they were both able to 'ignore it' for some of the time because of the nature of his moderate but improving hearing loss. Their philosophy was similar to the previous couple in the sense that both gave the impression of hoping that the problem would go away if it was ignored for long enough. It almost has a superstitious ring to it. There is another aspect for the second couple, however: that of feeling it is a bad thing to make too much fuss of a disability. As it happened, they both worked with animals – he was an inspector for a national animal organization – and both talked of not being sentimental with sick animals. Perhaps this approach was one they felt had relevance. Certainly at another point in the interview, the wife said she deliberately did not show her husband too much sympathy 'as it only made him worse, he laps it up'. He had previously been very ill following the road accident which caused his hearing loss. So they had been through a period together when they had obviously had time to evolve a clear-cut approach to illness and disability. They had been forced to confront the possibility of the husband being paralysed permanently so had decided on their joint 'policy' as a result of this. They referred to this period and their experience with sick animals as shaping their ideas about how to deal with illness and disability.

COMPARISON OF DEAFNESS, BLINDNESS, AND OTHER DISABILITIES

'You'd never say to a blind man, here, have a look at this, would you . . . whereas with me, people often say "pay attention, listen"' (73). This marketing manager in his 50s felt that the lack of sympathy deaf people received as compared to blind people was because of the lack of visibility of hearing problems: 'if you don't know they're deaf, there's no way of knowing'. Presumably he means until communication breaks down. He did not feel though that the 'poor press' deafness received in comparison to blindness was the only way deafness lost out; he said later in the interview: 'When Vera annoys me by walking away when she's talking to me, I say "Pity I haven't lost a leg or something because you can see that"' (73).

Blindness however is the disability most used by informants as a comparison with deafness: 'I think if I had the choice of deafness or blindness, I think I'd choose to go blind. I think being deaf you're cut off completely, talking every day is part of life, if you can't communicate with people, that's it' (30). This woman, the full-time mother of young children at the first interview, felt very bitter about her own hearing loss in her 20s and had been very depressed at its onset. She complained of feeling cut off herself and was finding life very difficult and saw hearing impairment in a very negative way. In contrast another man said that, although he saw his own hearing loss as a disability:

> I think blindness is different, worse than deafness. I'd rather be able to see than not hear – even if I can't hear, I can watch TV and people can learn to lip-read, before I had the hearing aid, I was picking up bits of what people were saying on the TV and persevering. (49)

This labourer in his 50s saw deafness in a positive light next to blindness and was optimistic about coping with the effects of losing his hearing. However this was during the second interview when he claimed his life had been 'transformed' by the wearing of a hearing aid after twenty years of being by, his own admission, 'withdrawn'. It is no exaggeration to say he and his wife were euphoric following this change in their lives: 'It's given me back my husband', the wife said. These two examples illustrate how perceptions of people's own situations are linked with their views of disability.

Two people in the group of informants had actually experienced some degree of both hearing and visual impairment. One man, after a successful operation on his hearing, was registered as visually handicapped and felt he took the hearing loss more lightly now because of having to cope with the visual problems. The other man having been injured in a bomb blast and prepared for complete loss of vision after a few years of eye problems was 'devastated' by completely losing all hearing as a result of the same incident. This cruel irony had left him unemployed and finding life difficult. It was his wife who said:

> I think of the two things, I think you could cope more with blindness, what it is, somebody once said *blindness cuts you off from things*, deafness cuts you off from people. I'd rather have the people part if it was me, I'd rather not see than not hear. (1)

For this young couple, in their late 20s, with young children when the hearing loss occurred, the negative view of deafness compared to blindness did again seem related to their own experience – they had been 'cut off' from people: the husband missed the company at work, had stopped going to other people's houses, and their conversation had become limited. Even though they were both trying hard, the 'people part' was increasingly lost to them.

Blindness was the most often mentioned disability and the comparisons did seem related to people's own experiences of hearing loss.

Disability was also mentioned in another context to illustrate another aspect of losing your hearing, how the rest of the family reacts.

> I don't feel I'm the odd one out. Say if you've got a person who is physically handicapped in a wheelchair the family revolves around that person and does extra for them. I don't feel that way. I'm still in charge of the family and a member of the family. I'm special in that I'm dad, or her husband but I'm not special because of my hearing, there's nothing extra special about that, that's how I see it. (71)

This man felt that although he acknowledged elsewhere that his hearing loss was a disability, it was not one which meant he commandeered extra attention from the rest of the family. Indeed he was very confident about talking about his hearing loss, talking of changing his hearing-aid battery in mid-sentence, in public, a very unusual attitude in the survey. He extended this attitude not only to his family but to the public sphere where he still gave talks despite not hearing the questions at the end very well. What is interesting here is the notion of 'special', emphasizing that it wasn't his disability which made him special but his other qualities.

Another family where one of the children had spina bifida made a different point about physical disablement. The hearing wife in this family said about her children:

> They're very aware of the situation because with having a disabled son we've got this sort of thing going in the family anyway so if anyone has got a disablement I think we are quite sympathetic anyway. As we said, at times you forget then that can be upsetting. (63)

So, for this family, hearing loss came into a general category of physical disability (the husband agreed with this view) and took it on, using the same model that they used with their son – that the process began with sympathy for the person who had the disability and moved on from there. Obviously there were slip-ups but basically efforts were made on behalf of the person with the disability and if the non-disabled people did not remember to do something in the proper way it was seen as very much their fault, not that of the person with the disability. This is a very different approach from the 'ignore it, it will go away' school of thought or the 'he doesn't try to listen' approach to hearing loss which has been discussed elsewhere.

PITY AND SHAME

It has been noted that seeing hearing impairment as a disability or not results in differing responses from hearing people who are sharing the lives of the hearing impaired. For some hard-of-hearing people it results in strong pressures of blame for their lack of effort. This is more often allied with not seeing it as a disability. If someone is accused of 'being able to hear when he or she wants to' then it implies that it is something that they have some control over and is therefore 'their own fault' if they do not hear what is said to them. This is discussed at greater length in Chapter 10, in the section on 'Effort and perseverence'. This blaming approach to not hearing is the opposite of the 'disability' one where it is something the sufferer cannot help. It differs in its effect on behaviour from the shame model. The word shame has been used in two different ways, one the feeling of being 'ashamed' and the second the feeling of 'pity' aroused in other people (it might be called the 'Isn't it a shame' syndrome). This interpretation takes on aspects of Talcott Parsons' 'sick role' in the sense that people who have access to the label 'hearing-impaired' are not held responsible for their actions in the same way as 'normal' people. This model would define hearing loss as being beyond the control of the people who are experiencing it. The disadvantage of hearing loss being beyond their control is that it takes away a lot of their sense of identity and control over their own lives. Adhering to the 'disabled' view brings its own penalties, one of which is the stigma of being labelled disabled and therefore 'incompetent' in some situations or 'incomplete' physically.

A woman in her 30s who had been very upset at a severe hearing loss when she was 22 years old described the feeling of being incomplete physically very well: 'I used to feel I was deformed. It's a deformity, something to be ashamed of' (89). This attitude had meant that she had stopped going out and had been completely 'withdrawn' in her own words. She even stayed in the bedroom all evening if her husband brought people home from work. Eventually she decided 'for the sake of her husband and the children' that she had to alter her life drastically. The way that she did it was to change totally her attitude towards the hearing loss. Whereas in the past she had hidden both herself and her hearing loss, now she reviewed how she felt about both attitudes: 'Now I class it just as wearing spectacles. I say to the children (who's been teased at school about her hearing impairment) – 'Tell them it's the same as spectacles, what's the difference between having bad eyes and bad ears'?' It also meant she changed her approach to disclosing her hearing loss to other people: 'Now I would say to people, if I don't hear you don't think I'm being rude, just attract my attention – I tend to point out my deafness to people first' (89). For this woman whether or not she saw her hearing loss in terms of 'deformity' was one of a number of factors. When she saw it as a deformity she felt ashamed and disfigured by it and quite unable to mix with other people. When she reviewed her 'deafness' and saw it as something 'matter-of-fact' like poor vision, she felt able to change her behaviour. The precipitating factor that made her change her behaviour was her realization that she was limiting her own life and that of her family. Part of her change in behaviour was altering her view of the 'disability', a term she used herself, to an 'everyday' accepted one rather than a stigmatized shaming one. The only time she felt that 'same sense of shame', at the time of the interview, was when she thought of her children bringing home a girl – or boyfriend when they were older. Then she said she could get very upset thinking about how they might be very ashamed of her. She still had remnants of the earlier attitude.

The sense of shame is brought up in another context by a hospital porter in his 50s who found it very hard to adjust to wearing a hearing aid – he tried to avoid wearing it because he said he felt 'ashamed'.

> Really it's thinking I look a bit disabled I suppose, it's a silly thing to say really but I don't know ... it's because people with good hearing have got an advantage over you. ... Since I've had the hearing aid it's hit me more about being hard-of-hearing – well I knew I was a bit deaf but how can I put it, since I've had the hearing aid I feel I'm more deaf, do you know what I mean? (24)

This illustrates several points, firstly that the hearing aid made him feel 'disabled' which he hadn't before. Secondly, because it is a visible sign of disability he felt at a disadvantage with hearing people, more than he had before. Is this because he feels he is admitting to a weakness by having the hearing aid? Thirdly it emphasized to *him* that he had a disability as well as to the outside world. He did not like telling people that he could not hear properly and did try to hide it. At the same time, however, he spoke of admiring a young woman he'd noticed at work who wore her hearing aid 'even with very short hair' (he'd grown his own longer to cover his hearing aid). He had not spoken either to her or to another man at work he'd noticed with a hearing aid, because he felt too nervous to do so. His view of disability linked up with his own reluctance to admit that there was anything 'wrong' with him. He had only been to the hospital because his family and friends at work had 'forced' him into it.

A clear cut rejection of the shame model is expressed by a man with a hearing loss talking about how his wife tells him when he's got something wrong. She says: 'You fool, no.' She said at the interview 'I don't say it tactfully, I don't think he'd like it if I was tactful', and the husband agreed: 'No, I mean this is not a *disease*, it's nothing to hide so what the hell' (56). He felt very strongly that it was not something to be ashamed about nor to be treated with care or pitied. He felt it should be treated matter-of-factly with no attempts to spare his feelings. This is very different from the earlier accounts given. Comparisons with other sorts of ill-health are made in Chapter 13 in the section on health.

THE DISABLED ROLE

Extending the 'disability' model to deafness means extending some of the protection afforded by that role and also giving up some of the rights that go with being able-bodied. One woman describing her hard-of-hearing husband showed this very clearly when she spoke of him in the following way: 'In a way you've got to look after *them* and take care of *them* really, don't tell him that, mind! He's just a big kid really' (71). By *them* she meant 'deaf people', the term she used. She referred constantly to doing things for her husband. He, in turn, referred to how his family teased him all the time and made fun of him. He said he 'expected it' though and did not 'expect any different'. He had concealed his hearing problem for years whilst in the army. His wife seemed to be saying that she 'looked after him' as a way of offering him protection because of his 'disability' which made him vulnerable. This could be linked to dependency when the disabled role is seen as clearly as this. The hearing partner takes on the role of 'carer'. Another husband talking about his hard-of-hearing wife said: 'I've always made the decisions because of her disability'. The wife disagreed: 'But you like making the decisions – it's you. I think if I'd had to make decisions, if I'd had an inadequate husband I would have. I've leaned on you a bit, I think a lot of people do irrespective of any disability they may have.' He replied: 'That's quite true, but I think over the years it's because of the position I've been in because of your disability' (8).

He saw his being 'on top' as related to her hearing loss. She disagreed. When interviewed one year later after she had been wearing a hearing aid (following years of poor hearing) they both agreed that she was 'transformed' and he'd got his 'come-uppance' as she now took a much more active part in decision-making and in life generally. The husband during the second interview summarized this change very clearly:

> She got more direct (since the hearing aid) whereas before she was very negative. She'd say 'you do it'. So in the end, I was bouncing around as if I was a little god in the house. It added up to giving her a lack of confidence and sense of inferiority and I used to take advantage of it, obviously, subconsciously. (8)

He felt he had dominated his wife to an unreasonable extent because of her hearing loss and that she had allowed him to take over. The wife agreed with this estimation, saying that she had never realized how 'deaf' she was until she'd got the hearing aid. The wife agreed then that her husband's behaviour and her own had been related to her hearing loss. He had taken on the role of protector and she had slipped into a more passive role because of her hearing loss. Fear of this same sort of dependency was expressed by a very self-confident man in his 30s:

> I've never told her but I fear becoming dependent. I always get her to take things back and complain for me. She gets angry but it's because I don't want to look stupid. I hate asking her to do it or make phone calls, you feel so useless. (14)

He felt diminished by even this very limited dependency. This fear of being made to look foolish in public outweighed the dislike he felt of asking his wife to do things for him. In all other ways he was very independent and appeared very much 'in control' at home. For him the dependent role was a very unpleasant part of his hearing loss.

Another husband spoke of taking on the protective role with his wife in a very clear cut way: 'I'm with her as much as I can' (76). He felt in order to 'protect' her he had to be with her as much as possible, saying: 'You've got to be their ears' (76). He typified hearing-impaired people as dependent when he talked about them generally and particularly saw his wife as dependent. In fact, when she could not hear at all (her hearing fluctuated) she said: 'My life comes to a stand-still. I stopped work, I stop in all the time, I won't do the shopping even' (76). She colluded with this helpless image and shared the view of her husband. It is interesting to look at gender differences in interpreting hearing loss as a disability. The element of gender may well be important. In a 'traditional' male–female relationship, it seems that women more readily accept the label of dependence with its undertones of incompetence and men might more readily attribute it to their female partners. However, in terms of disability roles and the way that behaviour is affected, men may *expect* more nurturing than women and therefore are more likely to expect people to put themselves out in order to accommodate their needs. Women are perhaps less likely to expect people to change their behaviour to suit them. This certainly seems to emerge from this study and will directly affect the role of the hard-of-hearing person in the relationship. This means there is a complex set of influences at work here. Gender is a vital element in interpreting disability.

DISCUSSION OF DISABILITY

There is a marked reluctance to accept the label of disability for hearing loss. There are no particular gains to be made by taking on this particular label. 'Hard-of-hearing' or even 'deaf', as has been demonstrated, do not generate particularly good responses from the normally hearing population. In common with other disabilities there is a desire not to be seen as only a disability, lumped together under such a terms as 'the deaf'. In mental handicap, putting people first as Ward (1983) points out does make a difference. Using terms such as 'people with a mental handicap' rather than 'retardates' or the 'mentally handicapped' is an improvement. For people who are hard-of-hearing it is particularly unwelcome to be classified as 'the deaf' when they feel their needs are quite different from pre-lingually deaf people. To have the stress laid on only that part of you that does not function well must diminish any sense of self-esteem. For people whose hearing is poor there are no particular rewards to be gained by identifying with this disabled group either. Hearing people are likely to be unsympathetic and unhelpful. There are, for the most part, unlikely to be any welfare benefits payable or access to particular services. Except in the case of severe or profound hearing loss, this group is not able to register as disabled and thereby receive any benefits or 'rewards'. It seems that the disabled role is rarely taken on completely by hearing-impaired people, although some of the aspects of being labelled as such are 'borrowed'. This 'borrowing' includes not being held responsible for not functioning perfectly and expecting sympathy and support from 'normal' people. A sense of stigma is perceived by hearing-impaired people, sometimes to the extent of preventing them fom disclosing their 'problem'. Hearing-impaired people are therefore most likely not to wish to be seen as disabled.

AGEING

One woman in her early 30s said: 'I don't tell people [that she has a hearing loss] unless I'm having difficulties. It's because of the embarrassment I think, being young as well, you usually associate it with older people' (30). She admitted that this attitude had been because 'I just didn't want to accept that I was going deaf.' She had been depressed and had been taking anti-depressants during the period following the hearing loss. For this particular woman the association with ageing was just another aspect of the negative and stigmatizing effects of losing her hearing.

A 57-year-old architect with a hearing loss for over thirty years felt the ageing image of hearing loss was a positive advantage, especially at work. He said

> I think I've got to the stage now where I'm not so self-conscious about it. I do tell people 'well I'm getting on a bit now'. I work in a crowd of people that tend to be a lot younger than myself, so it's easier to say things like that because 'I'm getting on a bit now'. (114)

He felt more able to admit to not 'catching everything' that was said because he saw it as more acceptable now that he was older to admit to a weakness which could be seen as a 'normal' part of ageing – not an abnormal one such as being disabled.

Another man felt more positively about his own loss because of his own ageing. He saw it philosophically at the time of the interview. 'I used to have a very keen ear but age doesn't come alone ... I've been less irritable when I realized that when I had to start wearing glasses as well, Anno Domini was doing it, so I just accepted it' (120). Previous to this he had strenuously rejected any idea that there was anything wrong despite family arguments with his teenage children and recognition that he 'looked at people's lips' when they spoke and 'sort of gathered' what they were saying by 'reading their expressions'. Ageing provided a reason for accepting this behaviour as a response to hearing loss.

For another man of exactly the same age it had the opposite effect. He was a television engineer so was constantly being embarrassed by bending down behind the television set (when he visited people's homes) and not hearing anything that was said to him. He had previously had a hearing loss which had been rectified by an operation but which had now worsened again. Another man had more trouble as his loss worsened a second time, according to his wife: 'He's not adapting as well as last time, because he associates it with old age now, he thinks he's got one foot in the grave' (42). He perceived his hearing impairment as part of a downward slope towards old age when it happened for the second time in his late 50s. He agreed that he did not 'accept his deafness' at all and that it caused a lot of tension at home. Growing older was not a consolation for him, nor was it reassuring that it might be happening to other people of the same age.

The mother of a teenage son experienced this negative combination of hearing loss and ageing.

> He can be pretty horrible if I've asked him three times what it is he's said and he's still mumbling. He says 'Mum you're turning into a deaf old lady'. He's at that age [14] when he feels he can say anything to me. I think he would really like to have a mum who is blonde and about twenty and it's disappointing that I'm going grey and a bit deaf. All that sort of thing, he can't quite take it ... it must be upsetting I suppose in some ways, you want your mum to be a glamour girl or something to show off to your friends at school. (68)

Her son had unrealistic expectations but she nevertheless feels sensitive to the implication that she, his mother, is 'past it'. Hearing loss is added to growing older as another factor in appearing a less attractive mother to this son. Does being hard-of-hearing make anyone less glamorous? This woman might well get the feeling it does, from how she interprets her son's behaviour.

The rise in the age of the UK population increasing the number of people with a hearing loss means that this will become a more and more important issue. In the meantime the response to decline in hearing at an earlier age does link up with stereotypes of old people with ear trumpets and jokes about elderly people who are deaf. Social attitudes to the elderly while negative initially are likely to be reinforced by a hearing impairment. Younger people then become older by association.

OTHER PEOPLE WITH HEARING LOSS

Beliefs about hearing loss are influenced by the experience of other people with a hearing loss. Most commonly people talk of 'deaf people', putting everyone with a hearing impairment in the same category. Whereas of themselves they either rejected any label or chose 'hard-of-hearing'. So the description 'the deaf' is used here. Attitudes towards other deaf people (apart from those revealed by the Bunting questionnaire showed a variety of different responses.

FAMILY HEARING LOSS

A few people in the study had direct experience of hearing impairment from in their own parents, not just as their parents grew older but during their childhood as well. This tended to help and was seen as a positive experience in their present situation. One couple where the wife's father and the husband's grandmother were hearing-impaired talked about their adapting to the husband's hearing loss; the wife said: 'His grandmother – she was stone deaf. It helped that we were used to it, but anybody that isn't used to it, is must be terrible' (49). This applied to the hearing person but for the hard-of-hearing person it may not always be so helpful.

Some people criticized the families they had grown up with because they did not deal with hearing loss very well. One hard-of-hearing man criticized his father who had the same problem for not 'trying' hard enough, for only telling him 'speak up' (126). Another couple criticized the wife's father who talked to his hard-of-hearing wife 'as though she were a child' (55). They were both conscious of trying to avoid doing the same thing in their relationship after the wife suffered a hearing loss in the birth of their first child. One hearing-impaired woman remembered her own father who during her childhood had been very isolated and (she now realized) 'left out of things' (68). She hoped her own three sons would be more sympathetic than she and her sister had been to her father.

Sometimes watching another hearing-impaired member of the family gave an example of how not to behave. One family teased a sister-in-law for not wearing her hearing aid. The hearing wife said to her sister-in-law: '"Where is it?" "In my purse" she said, so we all talked to the purse to make her wear it' (70). This teasing sounds very much a hearing person's type of joking. The hearing-impaired husband did not seem to have been involved in the 'joke'. He did 'disapprove' of his sister however for not wearing her hearing aid and she was constantly invoked by his wife throughout the interview as someone who was not 'trying' to adapt to her hearing loss. Family experience seemed to range from negative models of how to behave to providing valuable insights into the situation.

HEARING-IMPAIRED PEOPLE IN GENERAL

Attitudes to other hearing-impaired people ranged from matter of fact, 'they're just like anyone else' to pitying and patronizing. An example of this latter approach came from a hard-of-hearing woman in her 50s who said: 'That little deaf mute I worked with he drove a car – it amazed me how *they* could drive' (38). She had low expectations of pre-lingually deaf people, but she was unable to make clear the distinction of these groupings within hearing loss. She said at another stage in the interview 'I think that deaf people, God bless them, are very intelligent' (38). Her patronizing attitude was more strange because she was one of the few people who had had any contact with the deaf community. She had worked with two deaf people and had been involved at sports events with a team from the local centre for the deaf. She also said that she felt sorry for people who were born deaf because at least she had her memories of a time when she could hear. This seemed to imply that deaf people were cut off from building up memories or experiencing 'real life' by their deafness. A similar point was made by a much younger woman but with a different emphasis:

> What I think of to cheer myself up is to think of those little children with hearing aids. I think poor little souls, it must be terrible. At least I got through that part of my life. I often think I can't remember what it was like to have normal hearing, you just don't appreciate it when you've got it. I do feel for people who are deaf, they're a lot worse off than I am. (30)

This woman had been very upset by her own 'deafness' (as she described it) and obviously felt better for finding a group which was worse off. She did not reflect that pre-lingually deaf people might find it easier because they had not had to adjust to a *loss* of hearing. Interestingly she only selected children with 'hearing aids' to pity in this comment not those who were profoundly deaf. She herself found wearing her hearing aid very burdensome and stigmatizing. She did not seem to have any particular knowledge about deafness as she did not distinguish between partially-hearing children, or pre-lingual or profound hearing loss, but lumped them altogether as 'the deaf'. This woman used 'deafness' about her own hearing loss but 'dreaded' the day when she became 'really deaf'. She made a distinction between her own 'deafness' and being 'really deaf'.

There was a common tendency amongst hard-of-hearing informants to speak of 'people who are really deaf', sometimes citing our researcher who was profoundly deaf as an example. They often distinguished themselves from that category of deafness in a way that defined it as much worse than their own situation. As a group, the informants seemed to have a fair knowledge of the range of hearing loss. Most had no contact with centres for the deaf. Some had experienced deafness in their own family – either growing up with hard-of-hearing parent or having a child with 'glue ear'. Few had any hearing-impaired friends, although some had workmates who were hearing-impaired. Their response to our deafened researcher ranged from matter-of-fact acceptance to lack of understanding about how to communicate with him. Most people expressed interest in how he had become deafened. Having a hearing loss therefore does not necessarily make people more understanding or knowledgable about other deaf people in general. In common with other disabilities, sympathy was more often expressed for 'really deaf' people who could not speak than for hard-of-hearing people with similar problems to their own. Their attitude reflected general attitudes in our society towards disabled people.

LIVING WITH THE LOSS

This chapter has examined how people described the experience of hearing loss – what it felt like for them to lose their hearing and to use a hearing aid. The attempts of the hearing-impaired to communicate their experience to the hearing people closest to them and how that was understood revealed a widespread conviction that this was not easily achieved. Finding out what was wrong with their hearing and the way this was accomplished did have a bearing on the way the hearing loss was absorbed and acted upon. The gradual nature of most hearing-impairment was also important in this process. Making sense of any 'diagnosis' from health workers or of any change in the level of hearing was influenced by how hearing loss in general was interpreted. The main distinctions in making sense of hearing loss were between seeing it as a disability or not. Once defined as a disability this had repercussions for the behaviour of the others in the household. The hearing impairment was seen as not being the fault of the person concerned and being beyond his or her control. The opposite point of view sometimes prevailed where the hearing loss was not seen as a disability. Some people felt easier assuming that their hearing problem was neither permanent nor a disability. This seemed to reassure some informants who expressed the hope that 'it might go away'. This attitude influenced the way people behaved as it meant they did not adapt their behaviour nor expect those around them to do so. Some people interpreted hearing loss as a disability but most were reluctant to do this. There were very few benefits to be gained from taking on this particular 'disabled' category of hearing-impairment. Hearing people were unlikely to change to a more co-operative way of behaving. There was no particular sympathy given to hearing-impairment as opposed to the perceived sympathy to blindness. Aspects of disability were discussed by informants though in the sense of feeling imperfect or a lack of blame by others for their behaviour. The understanding of hearing loss varied according to experience with other hearing-impaired people, especially within the family. Stereotypes of hearing-impairment in general held by the informants were very similar to what we would expect of any random group in the population. They showed a marked reluctance to identify with people who were pre-lingually deaf.

The description of the loss from the viewpoint of the families interviewed shows that its impact can be severe even where little treatment has been sought. People's lives change in many different and complex ways. The differences may seem like contradictions but have to be taken into account if we are to reach a full understanding of the effects of hearing loss.

Living in a hearing world

Unlike people who are pre-lingually deaf those who are hard-of-hearing do not in general become part of the 'deaf community', in the sense of belonging to a centre for the deaf, or identifying with deaf people, or adopting sign language as the preferred means of communication. Only one of the couples interviewed ever used sign language at home and then only as a last resort to support speech. They were the only couple who had been to a centre for the deaf, and they had been there only to attend a sign-language class (not to mix socially). One other young man had tried to learn sign language, not very successfully he felt, and had been working as a volunteer in a mission for the deaf. His only close friend he said, was someone who was pre-lingually deaf.

In Campling (1981), one author who was hard-of-hearing wrote about 'changed camps'. She talked about watching a group of animated deaf people using sign language in a restaurant, when she had first become hearing-impaired. She decided to cross over to the other side by identifying more with the 'deaf community' and choosing to use sign language. In the hearing world she was struggling to keep going, to keep her identity. Seeing the animation of a group of people signing made her recognize her own lack of relaxed communication. However these people were unusual and most stay firmly in the hearing world where speech is the primary method of communication. They must rely on lip-reading or the written word. In this section we examine hearing-impaired people's experience in the hearing world. This chapter concentrates on contact with other people in both the private and the public world.

DISCLOSURE

A first concern outside the home is disclosure to strangers. Should one tell others of the deafness or should the partner tell? How the hearing loss is presented to new people (if at all) very much depends on how that hearing loss is viewed by the sufferer.

The wife of a man who was profoundly deaf and having problems coping said 'I have never to my knowledge heard him say to anyone "I'm deaf"'(1). They both described situations where others walked away, confused, when they tried to converse with the young man. Other informants however expressed great confidence in telling people, usually in a matter-of-fact way. A salesman in his 50s said:

> If I respond first then the embarrassment is taken away from that person. For the first two years I didn't really face up to it myself. I thought I would carry it off – because I was me, because I was good at my job and all that sort of thing. But I realize now that there are quite a few situations I go into where I've *got* to tell the person because if I don't, I appear to be an idiot, because I just can't really follow conversations. (41)

This is a good example because it shows a number of points about disclosure. This informant was conscious of the hearing person's point of view and sympathetic to it. He was anxious not to lose face and be thought stupid because of misunderstanding about his hearing loss. The same man said he sometimes began with – 'I'm not daft, flower!' because people so often mistook 'deaf' for 'daft'. He also highlighted the feeling that being hard-of-hearing could be compensated for by his accomplishments in other areas. Initially he thought this strong self-image would carry him through. Realizing that he would be diminished by being mistaken for having another sort of disability, intellectual impairment, was a greater problem for his self-esteem. He was realistic enough to know that to do his job properly he would have to disclose his hearing problem. He was also sensitive enough to notice people's responses and be aware that not taking them into account could ruin his sales figures. In a job that relied on communication this was a central issue.

Similarly another man, a mechanic, said 'I find if you tell people straight out you're deaf, they tend to help you, they make allowances for you' (17:2). This man felt he received more understanding about his hearing loss than he did about his heart problem which meant he got very tired very quickly. However he did say later on that he did not 'push himself forward' in conversation as it was 'too much bother' for people to try to talk to him. His hearing loss had fluctuated during the previous year and at one point had become profound. During the

152

period of profound hearing loss he said that writing things down had been 'alright at home but you couldn't expect people outside to do it'. At the time of the second interview his hearing had improved and then he was talking more positively about disclosure to strangers, when in one way he had less to disclose. It was easier for him to say it when less was required from the hearing person in response.

Some people operated a style of *partial* disclosure, saying for example 'I'm deaf *today*', using the excuse of a cold or sinuses. This was more acceptable to some people even within their closest relationships. One woman spoke of her entire courtship being conducted with her husband saying he had a cold so couldn't hear properly (78). He was a chartered surveyor who did not wear his hearing aid because of embarrassment and fear of discovery at work. He denied his problems with hearing although his wife felt they were marked. Another wife commented on her husband's attempt to conceal his hearing loss in the same way: 'People get crafty, cover it up . When I first knew him he hid it, he'd ask me to swap over sides on the road. I wondered why when we were courting' (46). This couple had been married twenty-three years and this man had then suffered a sudden severe decrease in hearing which affected his work and home life a great deal. He was still at pains to try to conceal and found it difficult to 'come to terms with his hearing loss' (63).

Goffman (1963) would describe this concealing behaviour as 'passing' in a hearing world: people from a stigmatized group who choose to try and 'pass' as part of another more acceptable group. To a certain extent this is possible for some hard-of-hearing people. Unlike people born deaf their speech is normal so it is not immediately apparent that they are in any way 'different'. 'Passing' could involve being mistaken as 'snobbish', 'ignorant', or 'stupid' when conversational cues are missed. This is often perceived as preferable to being revealed as having a hearing loss: the penalties of not 'coming out' as hearing-impaired are far outweighed by the advantages of remaining part of the hearing world.

For people who avoid disclosure chance discovery can be very upsetting. The discovery of a hearing aid is often a trigger. A mother of two young daughters said:

> The other morning Amanda's friend called for her for school and my hearing aid was on the cupboard. My younger daughter came in with it and said 'Mum don't forget this' and I really got my hair off with her. It was because her friend was there. I could have smacked

her for doing it which is silly really, but I just don't like people knowing I wear a hearing aid, I don't know why, it's just embarrassing. The thought of people knowing because you associate it with getting old don't you? That's probably what it is. (30:2)

This woman spent a lot of time trying to conceal her hearing loss (represented by her use of a hearing aid in this case). She rationalized it in terms of ageing but she also felt 'dread' at the thought of becoming 'really deaf' for reasons which were not solely to do with ageing. The fear of her children's friends finding out was not to do with her children being teased (expressed elsewhere by another mother), but for her own sake. She used the same policy with her friends at work and socially. She felt this approach was not a good one and did wish she could change – especially at work. Talking about being at work she said:

It's silly, I think to myself why don't I just go in there and say look I'm deaf, if I don't hear you don't think I'm rude but *I just cannot bring myself* to do it. I just try and cover it up. (30:2)

She felt quite unable to disclose in a straightforward way, finding it easier to say if she didn't hear 'I'm sorry I didn't know you were talking to me'. Her strategy was to avoid any disclosure even though she felt this was wrong and she wished she didn't do it. Her husband 'left it up to her' whether or not she told people when they were together. She had previously said he would not be embarrassed by having a deaf wife if her hearing got worse but that she would find it harder to cope because of an embarrassment. She had suffered from depression because of her hearing loss and was still having difficulties. By the second interview she had started part-time work again after being at home with children. She felt this was an improvement, although she was still spending a lot of time at work worrying about being 'found out'. Lack of disclosure was part of a general negative attitude towards her hearing problem for this woman.

Worries about the penalties that might result from disclosure were explained by a deputy headmistress who was concerned about going to business functions with her husband and about working. She said:

The only time I felt really embarrassed and tried to hide it, apart from the business situation with my husband, where I felt I *didn't want to let him down*, was with my headmistress. She tends to think of any illness as a weakness so I would try to hide it from her because I didn't want her to think I was *weak* in any way, but to everyone else I kept making a big thing about it, telling everybody. (72)

Firstly this woman had a policy of selective disclosure, and her husband's business colleagues and her own superior at work, for example, were not informed. Secondly she perceived her hearing as somehow reflecting on the way her husband was judged at work. 'Courtesy stigma' existed as far as she was concerned. She would 'let him down' by revealing that she could not hear normally. Thirdly she did not reveal her problem to her headmistress because she did not want to show personal weakness. This woman felt vulnerable about work and was not able to hear children talking in assembly when she was reading prayers. She therefore felt doubly nervous of a situation where she anticipated a lack of understanding from her boss at work, and where she already saw herself as having difficulties. She talked in the past tense because her hearing had improved over the previous year due, she felt, to a change in diet. She believed an allergy caused her hearing loss and the severe asthma that she suffered. For this informant disclosure was a carefully judged process, which she adjusted to suit different situations. She estimated the effect it would have on other hearing people by evaluating their responses. Her main approach which she expressed as the 'right' one was to tell people at once. However, this policy was one she felt had disadvantages in certain situations so she altered it accordingly. The two situations she mentioned specifically both referred to being judged competent at work. The implications are the same as the informant in Chapter 7 who said: 'I never tell anyone who has rights over me' (60).

The element of judging hearing people's response influenced disclosure in most cases. A bad experience may well ensure that a hard-of-hearing person is much less likely to be open about their problems in future. A young man who worked as a gardener said:

A lot of people round here know I'm deaf, but if they don't I don't say. They calls you mutt 'n Jeff. I can't stand that. Some people can be very nasty about being deaf, they don't know what it's like to be deaf. When you get into company with nasty people it pays you to be deaf. (88)

He lived with his mother and his sister who was mentally handicapped. He led a rather sheltered life. From his conversation during the interview it would have been very hard for a stranger not to have noticed that he was hard-of-hearing, but he obviously felt that sometimes he could escape the unwelcome attention of insensitive people by hiding it. He tended to see his role as rather a passive one on disclosure – if people knew that was alright, but he wouldn't go out of his way to tell them for fear of ridicule.

This attitude of waiting until other hearing people noticed was stressed by a nursing auxiliary in another interview. She summarized it in the following way: 'If people see [her hearing aid] they say "Oh you've got a hearing aid" and I say yes because I'm hard-of-hearing – and that's good enough – I still don't advertise it, that's my business' (5:2). This woman, like the young man, took a passive role in relation to discovery but for a different reason. She saw it as a matter of privacy and nothing to do with anyone else. It did not seem to be related to fear of the consequences, because when she talked of visiting Jamaica where she was born and only telling her mother and aunt there she said: 'I didn't tell anyone else but even if I had, they would just accept it, because they are like that' (5:2).

This confidence that others would have accepted her hearing loss certainly did not change her behaviour or encourage her to feel able to disclose. When a niece asked her what she'd got in her ear, she reported that she told her very sharply 'to mind her own business'. She clearly felt the intrusion of anyone commenting on her hearing loss. It was up to her to control the amount of information available and who received it. This contradicts the impression given by her earlier statement about people noticing as being acceptable because she did try to control who knew. She had a vested interest in hiding it at work in a mental handicap hospital where she had been caught asleep on night duty when she hadn't heard the sister aproaching, so part of her caution obviously stemmed from that.

It is worthwhile to look at her explanation for not telling her boyfriend about her hearing aid. He had noticed and asked why she hadn't told him. She replied: 'I didn't feel like it.' He said: 'We're supposed to be friends.' She said:

> 'Yes I know but I don't advertise it.' He was shocked because I hadn't told him. It didn't bother him one bit. I knew it wouldn't but to me *I just wanted to keep it to myself* and my family. I don't know why, but I don't go around telling people. Maybe it's pride or maybe showing some deformity or something. I think people in my position do think that way – 'Oh, I'm different from other people'. I know we shouldn't because everyone has their own complaints. Its just part of life.

This section is worth quoting at length because of the number of issues raised. The woman concerned wanting to keep her hearing aid, as opposed to hearing loss, to herself and her family, and repeatedly commented on not 'advertising' it. Then, when she anticipated an understanding reaction this did not change her outlook, either with family or friends. Even when it obviously upset someone she was fond of not to be told, she did not change her behaviour. Her worklife meant she tried very hard to conceal her hearing loss as she had good reason there to feel she should guard her privacy. But at work she criticized another hard-of-hearing nurse on the staff for having the television on loudly, whereas she consciously avoided doing that because of fear that people might realize she could not hear properly. Her policy on disclosure then related to privacy, pride, and fear of revealing a 'deformity' as well as fear of the consequences of discovery at work. As a single parent of three daughters, she needed to keep her job and went to great lengths to do so by hiding her hearing problems. This woman's situation and attitude to disclosure is interesting because it illustrates the complex nature of how people devise their policy. It is not straightforward, changing according to the situation and according to assessment of the people concerned. Sometimes it depends on how the person views hearing impairment in general.

Sometimes there was an admission in people's explanations of the inconvenience of admitting to new people that hearing is less than perfect. If hearing loss is disclosed then something is required of the hearing person, some change in behaviour must be expected. To illustrate this a schoolteacher said:

> It doesn't embarrass me [to disclose] that's why I can't rationalize why I don't come out with it straight away – it doesn't worry me to say it, but I have to be forced into saying it. I think it's because it creates a hassle. (48:2)

She explained her reluctance to tell people in terms of the inconvenience caused, yet at the same time she was only too aware of the consequences of not disclosing. She had also experienced insensitive reactions to disclosure. She had left teaching because of her hearing loss but had actually been 'signed off' by the doctor as suffering from depression. She felt that this affected how her retirement had been construed by her colleagues:

I'm quite sure there are some members of the staff at school who think I'm pulling a fast one. Nobody has been in touch with me to find out how I am. To them, I'm not ill, to them really there's nothing wrong with me, bully for her, she's managed to get out of it, on a pension, best of luck to her, there's not really anything wrong. A deaf person is her own worst enemy, because they don't broadcast it, you don't put a thing across your chest that says you've got problems, you hide in a corner. (48:2)

Two points are linked here: the hard-of-hearing person's lack of disclosure and hearing people's response. She felt ignored by her colleagues and perceived this as a lack of understanding. At the same time, she was conscious of not having explained her own problems to them while she was still teaching. She had experienced real difficulty with discipline and keeping control. She was also convinced that other hearing colleagues would not have understood if she had explained, as she repeatedly said very few hearing people knew what it felt like to be deaf.

Disclosure was not a matter of having one common policy for everyone. However one self-confident hard-of-hearing man said:

There is one thing I would say to people – don't try to hide it. That is a big mistake, I haven't done this but people I know do, trying to hide your disability it's stupid. It's far better to let people know you have a disability – often people don't see your hearing aid. There is no point in not telling them. It doesn't affect my self-image in any way that I need to wear a hearing aid and in certain circumstances – so I just accept it. (58:2)

This was a very forthright, definite expression of a belief in the benefit of disclosure. There was no fear of the response, or fear of being stigmatized or diminished by revealing a disability. It was a rare statement of absolute faith in himself and others. This was a man who was self-employed and had no fear of dismissal from work although as a bokseller he did need to be able to communicate. In contrast, a man of the same age who had been forced to leave the Army because of his hearing loss said he preferred not to tell people because 'it gives people the wrong impression'. He had suffered a heart attack two days after starting a new job after leaving the Army and had been forced to change jobs again. He was therefore in a very vulnerable position in terms of employment. He felt that the effect he had on people was important. In his new job he said he felt more comfortable about telling older people than younger people as though they would be more understanding or perhaps he felt less at a disadvantage with them. The difference in these last two men's views of disclosure derives from their view of themselves as well as their view of disability and their position in the labour market.

It is important to take into account all the factors, self-image, view of disability, expectation of response, rewards and penalties of disclosure, before deciding in therapeutic terms whether to encourage disclosure as a standard practice. A hard-of-hearing person's view of all these factors must first be understood.

MECHANICS OF EVERYDAY LIFE

This section is designed to give some idea from people's own accounts of what life is like with diminished hearing. What is everyday life like, what happens when you wake up in the morning? 'First thing in the morning I say hello when I put in my hearing aid and last thing at night, I say "have you anything else you want to say, otherwise goodbye"' (94). It is almost as if this man disappears once his hearing aid is off. He certainly talked of being 'completely out of action' when it was broken.

The idea of 'switching on and off' is a common one with hearing-loss sufferers not just hearing-aid users. People talk of the advantages of being able to 'switch off' completely to 'concentrate absolutely with no interruptions', and even of not having to join in unwelcome conversations.

CONVERSATION

One of the main negative impressions given of daily life is of exhaustion because of the efforts required for conversation and communication. 'I'm struggling, I find it very hard, very tiring. It's like three times as hard a day's work as it used to be [before the hearing loss]' (17). This was how a lorry mechanic described his work life following a sudden hearing loss. A similar comment was made by the journalist mentioned before (who'd given up full-time work since his decline in hearing). He said:

It's very hard work you know, when you're deaf, talking to somebody. I'm trying to hear what they say – you don't have a relaxed

159

conversation with someone if you're on the edge of your seat and you're watching and listening and thinking 'Did I hear that right' and 'sorry, what did you say' and it's all a job and at the end of it you think oh heck, I've got to sit on my own, get my breath back.(94)

Daily life and conversation were tiring and laborious in these accounts. A description came from a man in his 30s about getting up in the morning. He said: 'I turn on the radio and I can't make out what they're saying, it's all sort of fuzzy edged' (62). In trying to describe his considerable hearing impairment another man said: 'It's like listening to French when you're only learning it – you can understand some of the words but not all of them, so you quickly lose the thread of what's going on' (71). They were both talking about moderate hearing losses and this seems to give some idea of how conversation appears to someone who is hearing-impaired. Another man, a driving instructor who had suffered a sudden decline in his hearing after an operation on his ear, felt that he had a very good description of hearing conversation in a crowd which helped hearing people to understand. He told hearing people to imagine one piece of paper with writing on it, then another piece with different writing on it superimposed on top of the first paper.

> Now I say try and imagine reading that – you can see one lot of words through the paper and you would have to search for the other words all jumbled up together, they're all there and eventually you can get them – you imagine you are reading a sentence but all the words are on top of each other – well everytime I say that to somebody – that's how I hear people in a crowded situation – they seem to get the point immediately. (79)

This account conveys a similar image of knowing what the words mean but needing time to sort them into some kind of sense to that of learning a foreign language. A driving instructor felt his confidence slip away in company when he felt people were not understanding. He talked of the way hearing people he met socially disappeared once they realized what was wrong with him. He said that he rarely talked to hearing people of his hearing loss.

Conversation can take on a new dimension with different rules and aims. Some of the differences are explained in this next quote: 'It's almost like playing for time [asking people to repeat], you've heard the question, it hasn't quite registered and you play for time to get a reply ready – you have to rethink the question and interpret it and then reply' (124). Listening to speech becomes an uncertain test of ability to understand correctly for all of these men.

The other view is given by the hearing partners in conversation who experience a different kind of strain, sometimes from endless requests for repetition or irritation. One woman describes conversation with her hard-of-hearing husband:

> He understands best when I say the least, when I abbreviate, say the bare essentials – I know it's bad for conversation but you've got to keep it sweet and short and to the point. No good beating about the bush of a conversation, you've got to go straight there. You've just got to let the other things go. (88)

The wife felt this cutting short of conversation was a loss to her as well as to her husband because she felt she bothered to talk to him less. They argued a great deal (they both said) and it caused friction between them and their children.

Another hearing woman described conversations with her profoundly deaf husband. She began by trying to use sign language which they were learning, then to finger-spell the beginning of each word: 'If that doesn't work then I have to put on the computer and print it out there, it's not perfect but it's easier than writing because you can never find a piece of paper when you want it' (1). Their conversation had diminished over the two years since his hearing had gone completely, and he now rarely spoke; during the interview he did speak and his wife said:

> It's quite a shock when he talks, he only talks when he has to (he will write to me now, stupid isn't it?) I always put it down to the fact that because they can't hear themselves, so they don't need to talk, we talk because we can hear what we're saying. (1)

She makes a distinction between the hearing and the hearing-impaired, typifying her husband's behaviour.

This woman was missing out on conversation from both points of view, her husband no longer 'spoke' to her (except rarely) and she cut down on the amount she talked because it was such an effort. Her husband also felt unable to join in social outings and had not even felt able to join her at the children's Christmas play. She felt sad about that, sitting there alone, 'noticing everyone else saying "isn't she cute" to their husbands, but if he'd been there, I wouldn't have been able to say it anyway, would I?' Communication would have been difficult, presumably because of trying to talk to her husband in the dark (although neither of them mentioned that). What seemed sad was that neither of them thought that sitting together to watch the play was worthwhile for them or the children or that a squeeze of the hand might have sufficed as a way of indicating that they were enjoying watching their children in a play. For these two people, daily life was laborious and described by the husband as like being 'in limbo'. Their means of communication was limited which must have increased their difficulties.

Another couple, where one of the partners was profoundly deafened, had similarly difficult daily lives but were more positive about it. The wife, deafened in her early 20s, complained about her (relatively new) second husband. She said, with great cheerfulness:

> He drives me mad – instead of trying to change a word, most times he will persist in saying the same word over and over again until I say I can't get it. He can't or won't learn to finger spell so I have to try and remember all the symbols for writing on my hand. (64)

Despite this poor means of communication, they seemed to manage very well and were still doing so a year later when revisited. They coped with the problems that her deafness brought but both expressed satisfaction with the quality of their life. There is an interesting insight into the practicalities of life from these two people giving their accounts of each side of an argument. The wife speaking said:

> Normally we get on not too bad but we do get annoyed with each other if I don't understand. I'm silly I suppose, if we're out in the car at night, I ask him a question, he answers me and I can't get what he's saying because of the dark.

The husband said:

> I take care not to ask her questions in the dark any more and then next time we go out in the car, she starts talking again. Then she gets annoyed when she can't understand. I get annoyed because she bothered to ask in the first place.

These accounts explain the problems of communication in the dark with a person who is deafened. They cannot lip-read because they cannot see. The hearing person has to adjust as has the hard-of-hearing person. Another aspect is the limitation on conversation. People talked about the loss of intimate chat. Talking over the day's events in bed at night was lost once a hearing aid was taken out. Others complained of the loss of whispered conversation; comments were made such as: 'Bedtime is strictly limited now' (27); 'The whisper is a non-event with Mary' (7); 'Pillow talk comes to a sudden end' (65). The other barrier to intimate physical contact is that if one partner wears a hearing aid it makes a noise if anyone comes near to it, severely limiting any approaches. 'It whistles loudly [the hearing aid] when I try to caress her so she has to take it out' one husband said.

The effort involved in conversation makes daily life tiring for many hard-of-hearing and deafened people and those they live with and ways have to be found to get around this. It is not just the obvious difficulties such as how to communicate or needing a light on for conversation but also the more obscure changes which sometimes exasperate. A man talking about his conversations with his hard-of-hearing wife said:

> What I do find difficult at times is that – it depends what you're talking about – but there are some times when you want to talk quietly, it adds to it, but I find having to talk at a conversational tone or above takes the *impact* off it. You know, when it comes out, it's almost *false*. (3)

He felt he was losing some of the subtle ranges of conversation, getting around it other than metaphorically 'waving a flag' when he wanted to say something important.

THE QUALITY OF LIFE

Some of the qualities used to describe what life is like for both groups of informants were embarrassment, isolation, and lack of privacy. Both hearing and hard-of-hearing people spoke of embarrassment. A deputy headmistress described very well the mixture of feelings involved in having a hearing loss: 'You're embarrassed by it, you're frightened by it and you try to cover it up at the same time' (72). The confusion involved in trying to manage these three things at the same time had meant she never really felt she'd 'come to terms with it'. Embarrassment was referred to by another man relating his experiences outside the home, at social events: 'I'd persevere first, see how I got on, I get embarrassed – I'd rather the wife told me after – I feel too embarrassed to say "oh, do you mind, [I can't hear]" because it's me butting in on the conversation' (24:2). His embarrassment was caused by his feeling that he had no right to be asking other people to put themselves out for him in order that he could join in. This was clearly related to self-confidence and self-image and also he felt he did not have the social skills to know how to intervene without causing offence. His needs were not important enough to merit disruption of the 'normal' flow of conversation. Also the response can never be predicted in those situations and most of the informants had experienced some sort of unhelpfulness in response to requests for repetition. This man also used embarrassment to explain why he did not wear his hearing aid. Another hearing-aid user described her attitude in a similar way:

> I just feel embarrassed wearing a hearing aid, it's on my mind all day long when I'm in work, that I hope it doesn't pack up on me, hope these batteries don't go, how will I get it out of my bag without anyone seeing, I'm always checking in the mirror to make sure it's not showing – I know it's stupid, it's the thought of anyone seeing that embarrasses me. (30:2)

It is not clear here what aspect of it is 'embarrassing' although it seems the fear of discovery is the major factor, that the embarrassment would come from someone discovering that she cannot hear properly and needs to wear a hearing aid.

Embarrassment in both situations is linked to fear of hearing people's responses; will they be unkind if they discover that someone is hard-of-hearing? They were very often right to mistrust hearing people's poor responses. When the hearing group talked about their embarrassment it was often for the same reasons – other hearing people's lack of understanding. The wife of a deafened man described someone new coming to the house to look at a car:

> I said 'he can't hear you' and I suppose I then expected him [the visitor] to realize and talk to him but then he [the husband] shut off and he stopped talking to him and I didn't help really – isn't it awful – I suppose perhaps I didn't want to embarrass him more by saying well, just talk to his face – but I was embarrassed, I just didn't think. I find it awkward therefore I shut up. (1)

Her own embarrassment was because none of the three people involved in the conversation described above knew how to deal with the situation – the deafened man simply 'shut off' and did not know how to rescue the situation, the wife 'shut up' because she was feeling awk-

164

ward, and the visitor presumably did not have the knowledge or resources to know what to do next. It is interesting that the wife saw it as her responsibility to stop the visitor from feeling embarrassed as well as conducting the conversation. She had previously complained about not 'enjoying' it when people talked to her and waited for her to pass it on to her husband as she found it confusing and forgot what they had said and she talked of feeling 'self-conscious' in this role. So embarrassment existed for the deafened, the hearing wife, and the hearing outsider.

The public sphere introduces new elements of embarrassment. Having a conversation on a bus or walking along a street had become a source of embarrassment for one hearing husband because of the way he and his wife communicated in order to compensate for her hearing loss: 'There's absolutely no privacy with Mary because of having to shout all the time, you can see people looking at you' (74). This lack of privacy resulted from the choice of shouting as a way of communicating with his wife but for both of them it brought consciousness of 'funny looks' from other people.

Another example of these 'sideways looks' was mentioned by a hearing husband: 'It can be awkward sometimes when it's somebody she doesn't like who goes by – she says 'there's so and so over there' and goes on and on about them and she's talking very loudly and just doesn't realize' (55). He was aware that people stared at them both. At other times when someone said 'Hello' to his wife outside the children's school he was conscious that they thought there was something wrong with her. His wife said she also felt embarrassed in the same situation because: 'They tend to think you're either simple or thick or plain ignorant.'

These situations caused embarrassment to all the people involved and most seemed dependent on the response of 'hearing strangers' who have little or no understanding of hearing loss. There is a marked fear of being misinterpreted or even despised because of the hearing loss. It is an interesting example of Goffman's 'courtesy stigma' here that the hearing people felt it applied to them too in some situations where the hearing loss is stigmatized. Hearing-impaired parents worried about their children being teased at school because of their problems or not bringing friends home. Both these situations occurred. The courtesy stigma applied to families of hard-of-hearing people.

The isolation of hard-of-hearing people was only occasionally apparent for families. A few people talked of the whole family missing out when the hard-of-hearing person elected to withdraw from social life, or more often both partners in a couple ended up not going out because one partner was hearing-impaired. But more often the isolation applied only to the hearing-impaired person. 'It's automatic that a deaf person is isolated if someone comes here and we're all chatting, you just wouldn't be the centre of it all, anymore' (35). This was how one schoolteacher described it feeling it was inevitable; she even talked of having done the same thing herself years before to a deaf family member: 'It was easier to talk to someone else rather than struggle to talk to her' (35). She accepted it as part of being hard-of-hearing that she would be left out of conversations of more than two people.

Isolation and embarrassment are just two of the descriptions used for life as a hard-of-hearing person. They are good examples of how interactive the whole process is. Both illustrate the dependency on other people's reactions in communication, not just those directly involved but also observers. The 'hearing stranger's' lack of knowledge and skills for dealing with hearing loss makes life more difficult for the hard-of-hearing person and for the hearing partner.

EFFORT AND PERSEVERANCE

One hearing partner's version of why it was useful to get help from the doctor or hospital indicated the amount of 'effort' being put into coping with the decline in hearing in these early stages: 'Make sure they go and get an aid – not go on and on, it makes you feel that they're doing something rather than making you do all the work.' (56) Comments such as 'he doesn't try to help himself' and 'she could do a lot more for herself by wearing her aid' from hearing members of the family reinforced this notion of making some attempt to 'do something' by going along to the doctor. At a later stage the same arguments were applied to hearing aid use – perseverance was seen as the positive behaviour and giving up as negative. Interestingly, this was matched by hard-of-hearing respondents' concept of the amount of effort they were required to make in conversations at home. When there was more than one hearing person, it was often described as simply 'not worth the effort'. Sometimes this was justified in terms of 'it's just women's talk, I don't want to know what they're saying anyway' (from a male hard-of-hearing respondent). At other times it was framed in a preference for other activities – 'I've always got my head stuck in a book' was a very common one.

Effort was seen in a different light as part of adaptation by another interviewee, a deafened man: 'You are on your own – your solution and salvation is in your own hands. No one can help you psychologically except yourself' (50). Views of who does the adapting to hearing loss varied. One couple raised this issue. The hard-of-hearing husband said: 'I've always accepted it [the hearing loss] probably because it was so gradual. But it's up to the others [in the family] to accept it as well' (84). His wife said later in the same interview: 'I think the person who's deaf must adapt themselves to it, they've got no choice in the matter, unless you've been deaf you don't know what it's like, to me it must be awful' (84). Confidence about how people felt about their adapting was reflected in both hearing and hard-of-hearing people's comments and showed what they thought adapting was about. A very gloomy view of the future came from one hearing wife based on her experience of the first stages of hearing loss:

I used to get depressed at first because he never talked to me. He came home and fell asleep after tea. I told him to talk more, he tried, but it was worse, he stopped. I dread the thought of him getting deafer – I'd be terrible. I'd get to screaming point – I don't want all that arm-waving stuff. ... I think you just would cope I suppose. (113)

Interestingly, this quote shows ambivalent feelings about the future, full of dread about it but thinking they 'just would cope' on another level. Her complete horror at the use of sign language perhaps reveals her uncertainty of how to handle her side of the process in the public as well as the private sphere. However, her view of 'coping' with the present situation seemed none too satisfactory for either of them and certainly raises the issue of how much of a need there is for some kind of advice service at the early stages of hearing decline.

NOISE

Life at home was made considerably more difficult for everyone be-cause of the noise level. This was the single cause of friction men-tioned most often between people living together. The most commonly described scenario was that in order to hear the television, radio, or music, the volume was raised by the hard-of-hearing person to such an extent that the hearing people could not tolerate the noise, neighbours complained if the walls were thin, and children already in bed in the evenings could not sleep because of the loudness of the sounds below. The hard-of-hearing respondents felt their family (or neighbours) were being unreasonable about their needs. The other point to be made is the lack of knowledge about environmental aids – very few people knew of, and even fewer actually owned, television amplifiers which would have actually resolved this problem effectively for the respondents and their families by amplifying the sound for the hard-of-hearing family member. The hearing members of the household were exposed to the stress of loud noise which caused irritation but matched the iritation of the hard-of-hearing person who felt their needs were not being met if someone complained about the noise level. One hearing wife said:

> It's bedlam – twenty times worse, [even with a hearing aid] it's still loud and unbearable, the glasses rattle, it drives me insane. ... I must admit it does get me down – the noise of the television mainly is my worst worry. I can put up with shouting or talking to him, but that television, it really gets me down. Some nights I just feel sick where it's so loud and my ears are drumming, I said *I am going to go deaf* now because it's so noisy! (19)

In contrast, the hard-of-hearing people felt let down by their families' lack of tolerance about the volume level. One man said: 'Why can't they understand that I *have* to have it on that loud?' One profoundly deafened woman summed it up:

> I get very annoyed if there's not a sub-title programme on and people are darting about in front of the television screen or doing something else distracting ... I'm relying entirely on my eyes to try and follow this damn film. I feel like making them sit through a film with the sound off but they wouldn't stand for it, none of them. 'Ooh, the sound's gone.' *So has mine!* I think really the other partner who hasn't lost their hearing – it would do them good to be deprived of their hearing for a week and find out just what it's like – that would give them just a little bit more patience, I think. (64)

The simple device of a television receiver would have solved both sides of this problem, for the hard-of-hearing informants with a hearing aid, at least.

The other problem associated with television or radio is the difficulty in hearing a conversation above the background noise. This was another cause of frequent complaint from hard-of-hearing people, that they weren't left in peace to concentrate on the television or radio. Interruptions made the following of the thread of a programme extremely difficult. The same complaint was made by hearing partners when they were watching the television. If the hard-of-hearing person interrupted them to find out what was going on it sometimes caused friction between them if the hearing person stopped watching or listening, to explain, and then lost the thread themselves.

Lack of relaxation for both partners results from these two problems – noise levels and the interruption of concentration on a television or radio programme. A very specific example of the need for relaxation was given by the hearing wife of a man who also had a visual handicap:

> You need somewhere you can go and scream about it and then come back for another month. You've got to get out, like with small children, you can get it out of proportion. You need the peace and quiet of getting away and giving your ears a rest – I take the dog out! (62)

CHILDREN

An area of direct contact with other hearing people is in the private world of the home with the children of the family. Dealing with children illustrated both positive and negative aspects of interaction. Problems with 'insensitive' children were made worse by a hearing impairment but some children displayed great resource and initiative at an early age in dealing with their parent's hearing problems. Some of the difficulties were age-related.

> What happens is they don't go to him, don't tell him things, they come to me, and because of that, I deal with it – I've had to, because he could get the wrong end of what they're saying and when children are younger, you can't get it wrong, what they're telling you, you've got to have it right because you have to respond correctly. (66)

This woman was talking about her husband who is hearing-impaired and her children who were 21 and 24 years of age at the time of the interview. This raises a number of issues about family communication. This woman felt that 'correctness' and 'getting it right' were all-important in communicating with her children. She referred back in her account to 'young children' as a time when the need for correctness is all-important in communication, yet continued this same

169

behaviour with a son and daughter in their 20s. Presumably older children are capable of establishing for themselves whether or not their conversation has been understood correctly. For children in this family, the 'habit' of talking to the mother was so well established that they may not have learned the skills of checking whether their father had understood them properly. For this wife, communication was largely to do with 'getting things right', not the wider aspects of communication, feeling included in the family or getting closer to another person.

They said at a later point in the interview that the children showed no appreciation of how difficult it was for their father, and that when they were younger there had been a lot of friction between the parents, about his hearing loss, which had upset the children. The parents said they had not explained to the children why there were arguments. This policy of 'protecting' the children both from wrong information and from the knowledge of what was causing the parents' rows seemed to mitigate against any understanding on the children's part of what their father was experiencing. This policy was combined with the model of their mother's self-confessed irritable behaviour towards her husband. The husband also said he had not wanted to admit he had a hearing loss. In the interview, he said he had only had hearing problems for ten years, his wife however, said twenty-four years was nearer the truth. This seemed an indication of his reluctance to admit the problem. This combination of behaviour from the couple had led to years of 'rows' which they felt they were now overcoming by effort.

This illustrates a way of excluding children from the central process of communicating with the person who is hard-of-hearing. The hearing adult not only acts as interpreter but also takes over responsibility from the hearing-impaired adult and becomes the main confidant for the children. The hearing-impaired person thereby suffers not only a hearing loss but also a loss of role within the family. If the children are not left to sort out communication with the hearing-impaired parent themselves and the hearing parent 'takes over' communication this can extend into other areas of family life and decision-making.

DISCIPLINE

A single parent felt her sense of being in control was important:

> I never have any problem disciplining them anyway – because I brought them up in a way that anything I say stands. They used to

170

say [before the hearing aid] they had said things to me and I said they didn't, so now if they say anything to me that's it. So now everything is on one level. (5:2)

This woman did keep a very firm grip on her three teenage daughters, something the daughter interviewed also recognized. However, she felt that the discipline she had managed to maintain had been threatened by her not being 'on the same level' about hearing. Before she had had her hearing aid, she had missed some things they had told her, but she stll felt she kept control. This mother was obviously relieved to have the hearing aid as a way of keeping that control. She never lost control even without her hearing aid but she was aware of not feeling quite so sure about it. Being a single parent avoided the possibility of another parent taking over – but even so, there was still the possibility of discipline slipping away.

One woman said of her husband's hearing loss: 'The children [aged 13 and 16] take advantage of him. It's a real problem, there's less discipline, they abuse it [the hearing loss]' (46). She felt this was a great change in their family life. She was as reluctant to take on the role of disciplinarian as her husband was to lose it. There was no sense here of the role being 'taken over' by the other parent, but rather that it was lost by the original disciplinarian parent. This may have been related to the ages of the children who were teenagers at the time of the interview, and therefore likely to be challenging this particular role anyway. The older daughter of the family did not lack insight though, although she said of her relationship with her father that they did not seem to be on the same wavelength. She also said: 'My dad still feels that he is different from everyone and he doesn't like people to know he is deaf – just because my dad is deaf, that does not make him change as a person' (46). She seemed very aware of the problems that her father was having and echoed his own sense of isolation and reluctance to tell other people about his hearing loss, as well as his wish to be recognized as still the same person.

Both the daughters in this family were closer to their mother but the father felt that was partly because he had really wanted sons so he had expected daughters to be closer to their mother. This justification did not seem to cover the comment that he felt isolated within the family since his sudden dramatic increase in hearing loss. He had previously had a mild hearing loss. When the sudden loss had occurred, the children had been small and had been frightened by his loud voice.

171

They had repeatedly run away when he came near them, according to his wife: 'He had gone to pieces' after this. It seemed that the severe hearing loss had begun in a traumatic way with no real support for the family from outside and they had had to adapt as best they could. This meant worries about discipline and closeness in the family. The relationship with the children was influencing the relationship between the parents.

ADOLESCENCE

Teenage children were cited repeatedly as a particular problem; but people reported children 'coming back' in their 20s. Their 'age' is often given as an excuse for teenagers' lack of tolerance towards their hearing-impaired parents. This excuse was used by a mother of a teenage daughter: 'My daughter and her boyfriend look at each other and laugh when I can't hear ... she's as bad as you can get, she couldn't get worse ... it breaks my heart but I just turn away' (23). Even though this behaviour was obviously upsetting, the hearing-impaired mother herself still excused it later on in the interview as being because of the daughter's age. This lack of sensitivity to her mother was made worse by colluding with another hearing person, to exclude her mother from the joking. The woman said her husband also left her out of conversations and that the husband and daughter talked to each other and excluded her. Only her younger son made any attempt to include her.

The 19-year-old son of another hard-of-hearing mother gave his account of the situation from the adolescent's point of view:

> You have to get used to telling her half a dozen times. I lose my temper after two or three times and walk out. We're not the sort to talk anyway, there's nothing important to talk about, so it doesn't matter – I treat my room like a bed-sit. (80)

The negative attitude expressed here was not only towards his mother's problems but also towards conversation of any kind at home. 'There's nothing important to talk about' seems a very final way of describing conversation between children and parents. How much of this attitude is to do with 'normal' adolescent behaviour is debatable – his negative attitude does seem to extend to conversation and home life generally rather than being specifically directed at his mother. Her hearing problem only seems to make it worse.

172

The same attitude was described from a mother's point of view, this time talking about one of her four sons in their teens and early 20s. She felt particularly despairing because she had had hearing problems for over twelve years. She talked about their lack of effort to talk to her:

> I never seem to register. I've been telling Bruce I'm hard-of-hearing since he was four ... they've done nothing at all to adapt ... I used to say to them 'put cotton wool in your ears and see what it's like' but they never did, whether it's because it's boys. I don't know whether girls would have been more considerate. (53)

This mother had withdrawn from the family to the extent of not going on holiday to Canada with them the previous summer, something they had planned for a number of years. Her account above shows that their lack of understanding was made worse by the fact that it did not alter over the years, nor did the sons try to do anything to understand how she felt. It seemed a rather faint hope to put it down to gender, that their behaviour might be more excusable because they were boys. Her husband for instance did not share their behaviour. He was more understanding, so she obviously didn't believe that men were incapable of being understanding. She did not really look for excuses for her sons, saying later in the interview that, apart from one, they were all extremely selfish and only thought about their own lives anyway. Their father said he thought they would change 'when they got married'. This woman played a traditional role in the family, she stayed at home, cooked all the meals, did all the housework for these four grown-up sons, something she commented on as perhaps being unnecessary at their age. Perhaps her lack of expression of her needs in other areas meant that her communication needs were also overlooked within this particular family. She did everything for them without comment so they did not expect to have to do anything for her in return.

The insensitivity and self-absorption of adolescence clearly has particular problems for the hearing-impaired parent when communication requires effort to be made at all times, not just when the young person is feeling particularly helpful. One man who had a sudden severe hearing loss said: 'If you didn't get on with your family to start off with, you've obviously got more of a problem' (81). He was acknowledging that any communication problems that were there already would only be made worse by one parent having a hearing loss. In his own case, he felt his teenage children had been difficult but had 'come back' as he described it. His youngest child, still a teenager, conducted conversations in the following way. He said:

> She talks to her mum and hopes I'm listening, she talks less to me as an individual – not together, it's something we haven't done for a long, long time which is a shame in as much as it can break down a family, family get-togetherness if you like. In other words, the family is still together but to start off with, the deaf person is slightly out on a limb. (81)

This description is not of the straightforward rudeness described earlier, but more of the subtle move away from the centre of the family experienced by the person with the hearing loss – feeling out of touch with children and missing out on some areas of intimacy. One woman described it as having 'lost a lot of my younger daughter' when she talked of her relationship with her child during the period of her hearing declining.

BEING AN INTERPRETER

Communication is not just a problem for the hard-of-hearing parent. Conversation becomes difficult for the hearing parent if they take a responsible role in the relationship. Sometimes they are put in a difficult position between the two – the other parent and the child. One hearing wife said:

> 'They [the grown-up children] come bursting in to tell me some-thing [like when Jennifer got engaged], then they get irritated when I stop to explain to Derek what's going on. I feel pulled both ways. I don't want to antagonise her (the daughter) or him (the husband).' (90)

The hearing parent here was acting as interpreter and feeling that demands were made on her by both husband and daughter with no recognition of the position she was in. Her role as interpreter/wife was conflicting with that of supportive mother. Both roles required her to give support yet she did not receive help from the daughter in explain-ing to the father what was happening. She was required to take on an impossible task. Because the communication was going through the mother, her role as interpreter was interfering with her own direct communication with the rest of the family. Communication was not just potentially threatened between the hard-of-hearing partner

174

and the child but also between the other hearing members of the family.

YOUNG CHILDREN

Young children were sometimes described as difficult because of night waking or poor speech. They were also described as helpful and considerate from a very young age, looking at their parents when they spoke and touching them to get their attention. There were age-related difficulties with each stage of childhood which can be traced in the following section.

In the maternity hospital

In Chapter 11, p. 192, a mother is quoted as being made to feel 'inadequate' in the maternity ward when nurses told her that the child should be taken away as she would be unable to hear it cry during the night (27). Other mothers reported similar experiences of having children taken away. One mother had asked a neighbour to wake her and had kept the baby next to her bed. This had worked perfectly well. Another mother had been told she would 'hear' her baby as it was a 'mother's instinct'. The woman's response was to say 'what rubbish!' and feel that no one had tried to understand her situation. She was then woken abruptly in the night and reprimanded for not hearing her baby. Waking a hard-of-hearing person at night is complicated by the problems of lip-reading in the dark and lack of a hearing aid when asleep. It is more difficult to understand what is happening, so the whole process needs careful handling. Another mother had arranged with a nurse to wake her gently when her baby cried. There seems to be a number of possibilities for managing this particular situation so as to avoid the unhappiness caused in the life of the first mother mentioned here.

Some mothers' hearing loss either occurred or worsened after the childbirth. 'I couldn't hear a thing for a whole week after Kelly was born but no one seemed to be interested at the hospital, no one wanted to know' (65). This mother had gone home to the difficulties of coping with both the baby and the hearing loss which, although it improved initially, declined later. When she consulted a new GP for a chest infection, and asked him to speak up because she couldn't hear it was only then that her hearing loss was recognized and acted upon. Until then she had been told by her GP and the hospital doctor that there was nothing wrong. Her response to her hearing loss initially was to withdraw from the outside world. Her early experience in the maternity hospital had not helped her to cope with her hearing loss at all. Staff did not appear to be familiar with hearing impairment so did not know how to deal with it.

The experience of childbirth and maternity care is an important area in the development of the relationship between mother and child and if this early stage is mismanaged both parent and child miss out. Knowledge of hearing impairment as part of health workers' training would undoubtedly improve the situation. In childbirth, for example, use of drugs such as pethidine makes it very difficult for mothers to lip-read as they lose their concentration. Having a nurse at the feet of the mother in labour means she cannot follow what is being said to her; another person should be at the head of the bed to explain what is happening. Training in communicating with patients who are deaf or hard-of-hearing could be included as part of health workers' education.

Children at home

Only one parent used a baby alarm so problems occurred. Two single-parent mothers relied on older children to wake them when the younger ones cried at night. A mother whose husband was a fireman and was therefore out at night said her children had learned about her hearing loss at an early age:

> They always knew that if they wanted me they'd have to get out of bed and come to me. They never just lay and cried, any of them. They've always grown up to know that they have to make me know they're awake and they need something. (89)

The children in this family soon learned 'hearing tactics'. They learned to touch their mother, face her, and get her attention before they tried to speak to her. This adaptability and resilience was commented on elsewhere. One mother said her son at fifteen months had learned to bring her hearing aid to her when he woke her in the morning and give her the aid before asking for something to eat. (It was more usual for mothers than fathers to report this.) Mothers often reported very young children pulling their mothers' faces around towards them before they spoke. Mothers reported that night times

176

were a problem because of not hearing changes in the babies well being. One mother (89) talked of a 'frantic time' when her eight-week old baby had whooping cough and she could not hear her choking and spluttering. The doctor had suggested taking the baby into hospital because of this but the mother had decided to keep her at home. It meant that she got very little sleep. Other mothers talked of worrying about babies with chest infections when changes in breathing were important. Hearing problems did not just affect the straightforward hearing of children's voices but also their coughing, snuffling, and other sounds. These signals of unease are part of a mother's way of interpreting their children's behaviour and is an area of potential problem for hearing-impaired parents. Communication with young children produced a number of problems. One mother said:

> I think the youngest was most affected, he jabbered a lot to me and I couldn't hear. I remember saying to Mr M. [the consultant] 'I can't hear what my three-year old is saying to me' and he said 'Well I should think that's a blessing' but it isn't because they're asking you questions and you know the frustrations. When he went to school and starting drawing pictures he'd draw a face and draw *great big ears*. I was always saying to him 'I can't hear' so it created an impression on him. (53)

This woman felt the consultant and the hospital dealt unsympatheti- cally with her communication problems with her 3-year old son. It was a very real problem to her and she felt it was dismissed. She felt very self-conscious about her hearing problem anyway and it was made worse by feeling her young son was aware of it. His drawings at school of faces with big ears were something that she reported as a source of self-consciousness for herself. She went to great lengths to hide her hearing loss and felt that no one at home understood it. Her hearing problems had begun badly with the young child and the situation had not improved. When interviewed her sons were grown-up and still not at all considerate. This early stage of parent–child communication needs careful nurturing anyway, so a hearing loss needs to be resolved.

For some people this early stage of communication is important enough to stir them into some action on their hearing loss. One man talking about his 4-year-old daughter said:

> I think the one person I felt isolated from was Anna because kiddies' speech is not clear anyway. Obviously to me Sarah and I were there on a basically parallel footing and Anna was slightly separated from

us and that was the reason I decided to have the operation. The child was trying to communicate with me and making no headway at all. (62)

He felt that his daughter's attempts to talk to him merited some effort on his part to try to meet her halfway. This problem of understanding was exacerbated by his having a visual handicap as well. Although he felt it did not affect his wife so much she felt it affected them all. She said: 'It was a general family thing wasn't it? It was becoming a problem to the family as such' (62).

Communicating with young children affects both parents if one of the parents ends up by becoming the interpreter and channelling all communication through the hearing partner. Another aspect of communication is the child's language development. A mother with a severe hearing loss said 'I had felt very upset when my son came home from school with a note saying his speech was poor and that he mispronounced words. I felt "it was all my fault"' (32). She felt she had let her child down. This was a woman who otherwise coped very well with her hearing loss. She worked as a driver for a bakery and expressed herself content with the situation at home. Her husband agreed – he said of her severe hearing loss 'We get on so well I don't notice it' (32). The generally good coping strategies that occurred in this family then only underlined the feeling of failure that this woman experienced about her son's speech. All three members of the family interviewed expressed themselves pleased with their communication otherwise. Parents widely reported young children's abilities to communicate well with their parents however without any sign of being 'taught'. One hard-of-hearing mother said: 'We never actually told the children but they sort of sensed it. If I didn't hear what one of them said they would come up to me, but they just seemed to adapt to it' (12). She felt that their children had adapted well without any particular effort on the part of the parents. Her husband agreed saying that the children now helped their mother to cross the road (the eldest was 8 years old).

CONCLUSION

This chapter has dealt with the reality of having a hearing loss and living in a hearing world in both the public and private sphere. It has looked at the problems of relationships at home with children and other adults and how the changes in communication affect both sides. The basic problems of noise in the home, the difficulties of conversation at all levels, and the potential difficulty with teenage children in particular have all been highlighted. Accounts of disclosure have shown how this varied according to situations and perception of hearing loss. For some people disclosure meant giving away information about themselves that they preferred to keep private. There was also a fear that this information might discredit them in some way especially in terms of work. The other problem was that disclosure did not necessarily bring a good response from the hearing person – it was unlikely that their behaviour would change to be more effective for the hearing-impaired person.

Perception of hearing loss was also important in terms of behaviour; beliefs about how much 'effort' was being made by either partner in a relationship very much depended on how the hearing impairment was seen. Accusations of 'he can hear when he wants' came from hearing partners who saw the hearing loss as within the control of their partners and not as a disability. There was often a desire by hearing partners for a sign that 'something was being done', 'an effort being made'. This often meant going to the doctor or hospital and getting and wearing a hearing-aid. This was perceived as a sign of the hearing-impaired person trying to do something, but sometimes resulted in an unrealistically high expectation of what could in fact be done. This was especially true of hearing aids, where there was little understanding of the difficulties of use. The hearing-impaired partners often felt similar feelings of frustration about the amount of effort made by their partners in communicating with them.

The level of noise in the home was the major complaint about everyday life for the hearing partners. The volume of television and radio caused a high level of tension between people living together. For the partner with the hearing problem this was perceived as a lack of understanding of their difficulty. Very little was known about environmental aids which could have helped the situation considerably.

Children proved to be a mixed blessing, as in other areas of life. Some were resourceful and full of initiative at finding ways around their parent's hearing problems. Others, teenagers especially, were reported to be lacking in understanding and any attempt to accommodate the needs of their hearing-impaired parents. There were widespread problems in maternity hospitals with mothers reporting feeling inadequate because babies were taken away because they would not hear them. Health workers' training in communication with the hearing-impaired clearly needs developing. There was evidence of unease at home because of night-time waking of young babies and resulting tension between parents. However parents did report children learning very early on to come and wake their mother or father who could not hear them or bringing hearing aids to them in bed as young as 15 months.

The insights revealed by these accounts point to a great deal more research being done on what the quality of life is actually like for people who are hearing-impaired. Which situations present problems? In terms of service provision understanding a mother's problem in childbirth or the maternity hospital, it would help to arrange health-worker training to accommodate the needs of such mothers. Any kind of hearing therapy requires more knowledge and understanding of the difficulties involved for hearing-impaired people in relationships with hearing people and just what their experience of daily life is like. It is tiring and complicated, and in many cases a strain is put on relationships, but there is plenty of evidence that people work out ways of coping with a hearing impairment. This source of expertise should be tapped to provide help for others in the same situation. A person with a hearing impairment should not be counselled alone all of the time; there is a strong need for working with the other members of the household, or those close to them. There is a striking lack of knowledge about environmental aids which needs to be rectified. Disclosure needs to be examined as part of the therapeutic process and the benefits carefully considered.

Learning from the people who are experiencing the situation is a valuable part of working out ways of coping with acquired hearing loss.

11

Relationships – in or out of the circle?

> You get cross with the people who are close to you that's the sad thing. You tend to think that people who are close to you should know better – I think you can be very unreasonable sometimes. ... Like last week, these hearing aids were hurting, I knew that was coming out in my dealings with Pat; because she happened to be here – she got it, whereas if anybody had come in, I would have been sweetness and light. (48)

This teacher, aged 48, recently had to give up teaching because of a gradual hearing loss. Here she describes very clearly the ambivalence felt towards those closest to you, when confronted with hearing loss. Describing the same day's events (trying to get used to wearing two aids) her partner said:

> I never know whether it's me that's upsetting her or it's just the hearing aids – I can see the thing that most infuriates her is the different volumes – she gets so frustrated – one minute it's too loud, the next it's too soft – but I don't know whether or not it's me. (48)

Shared perceptions of a situation are important since they shape the interaction of those involved. We know this is critical in close relationships – in fact probably the determinant of those relationships. As we have seen so far, hearing loss is a potential wedge between the participants in a relationship and we have been concerned to assess the extent of the problem created and how those people at home can come to terms with the change.

The questionnaire responses revealed findings about hearing loss, employment, and personal and social life and its changes. The next stage looks in more detail at how 'the family' views the change and how their individual perceptions come together to form a new system, accommodating the change brought about by one member of the household experiencing a hearing loss. In this section the system is examined directly from the joint interviews with family members. The particular focus we have used here is a joint task we asked of the partners: to arrange a series of blocks as symbols of the family relationships. We have examined their discussions of the task.

THE SPECTOGRAM

As we have seen in our discussion of the family (Chapter 3) there has been very little research concern with the partners in home life. Beattie (1981) found evidence of the development of 'protectors' or 'benefactors' in the family and developed some interesting side-points on the guilt and impatience as well as support found within families. The difficulty of looking at change in families is that there is little knowledge of the situation which existed prior to hearing loss – for example, if one partner deals more with the outside world this may always have been the case. Knowing what the family is like now does not tell us directly what might have been if hearing loss were not present. The technique we used is adapted from one which has been used by dramatherapists for some time and it allows people spatially to describe their relations as they see them now and as they perceive them to have been in the past.

The spectogram is a technique taken from 'family sculpture' in dramatherapy to allow people to show how they see the family. It involves using blocks of wood to represent each person living at home. We asked the hearing and hearing-impaired partners together to place the blocks spatially to show how they saw themselves in relation to one another and the others in the family. There were three elements of the task:

1 How they saw the situation at the time of interview.
2 How they saw it before onset of hearing loss.
3 How they see it in the future.

There were three levels of analysis:

1 The spectogram: what people were actually building with the blocks.
2 Discussion: the audio recording of what they were saying about it as they did it.

3 Observation: what they were doing as they arranged the blocks. (For instance, saying 'We are a close-knit family, the hearing loss makes no difference' when the hearing partner had his or her back to the person who couldn't hear, leaving them looking puzzled and left out.)

This is a technique which provides a great deal of data on relationships. Our examination of the outcomes of this analysis gives us a number of significant areas for discussion. While the patterns offered by different interviews tell us about the overall structure of the family, we have chosen to explore three areas further: intimacy, control, and relationships with children.

Table 11.1 The patterns of family spectograms

	At 1st interview (n=94)	At 2nd interview (n=29)
Close family, united	25	13
One person the central focus	10	0
Parents united but separate from children	10	0
One member protecting others from the world	1	0
One person 'on top'	7	0
One isolated member of the family	17	4
One parent/child alliance	5	0
Leading separate lives	8	11
Children a barrier between parents	2	0
Parents against children	6	0
Living alone	3	0

PATTERNS OF FAMILY LIFE

In each illustration which represents the agreed layout by the partners, the symbols are 1 for hearing-impaired person, 2 for hearing adult, and 3 and 4 for children. There are obviously many spatial patterns available particularly if we take into account the actual distances between blocks. However, it is possible to classify the spectograms into: united families; fragmented families; and families with an isolated individual.

Table 11.1 shows the distribution of family patterns. The first

Table 11.2   'Family' change as a result of hearing loss, recorded as a spectogram

Diagnosed group	%
Said their family had changed for the better	4
Said their family had changed negatively as a result of hearing loss	40
Said their family had not changed as a result of hearing loss	36
Said they had not known each other before hearing loss, so could not compare	12
Said it would become worse with hearing decline	7

Table 11.3   'Family' change as a result of hearing loss, recorded as a spectogram

Pre-diagnosed group	%
Said their family had changed for the better	0
Said their family had changed negatively as a result of hearing loss	14
Said their family had not changed as a result of hearing loss	55
Said they had not known each other before hearing loss, so could not compare	0
Said it would become worse with hearing decline	31

five are united, the sixth one is the isolated member of the family and the others are fragmented. The last item in the table shows the three respondents who lived alone. Not surprisingly there are many variations. A particularly significant one for our later discussions is where partners are not equal in status and where one dominates.

Obviously, all of these arrangements 'work' in the one sense that they are still functioning families, but we would expect certain patterns to be at risk when hearing loss occurs. We would predict that close, equal-status families would cope best in one sense because they are more able to empathize. However, on the other hand, they are more at risk since it is their equal-status, easy communication framework which will be most affected by the onset of hearing loss. Fragmented families would in this way be better able to cope since the changes called for may be less.

In Table 8.1 we saw that a significant proportion of people did not feel there had been change in life style, personality, or happiness. In the pre-diagnostic group only 7 per cent perceived change in lifestyle as a result of hearing loss as compared to 54 per cent of those with recencies up to 2 years and 67 per cent whose recency of hearing-aid issue was greater than six years. Our comments on change, therefore, mainly apply to those in this last group though where significant change ocurs in the other groups we will refer to them.

Tables 11.2 and 11.3 show the number of changes which had occurred as a result of the hearing loss. The most common change is a negative one in the diagnosed group. Some change was reported for the better, i.e. loosely-bonded to close (Figure 11.1). They actually felt they had drawn closer together as a result of the hearing loss in one

Figure 11.1   Spectogram of family showing drawing together after loss of hearing of one member

Before hearing loss

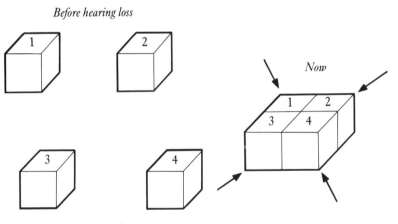

1 = person with hearing loss
2 = partner
3 and 4 = children

Figure 11.2   Spectogram of family showing increasing isolation of hearing-impaired member

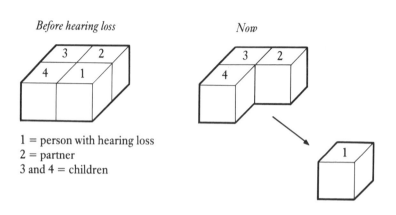

Before hearing loss   *Now*

1 = person with hearing loss
2 = partner
3 and 4 = children

case 'because of the effort involved', in the other because it was accompanied by another physical illness and coping with the two things at once made them feel that they should 'combine their forces' in order to deal with them. Figure 11.2 shows the commonest change reported (seventeen people reported this change). The new arrangement shows that the family had regrouped to exclude the person with the hearing loss. One comment on this pattern from a hearing wife was 'He's in a world of his own' (1). Figure 11.3 shows the presence of a 'relay-station' between the hard-of-hearing person and the rest of the family. Sometimes one member of the family stayed close to the person who had suffered loss of hearing and were reported as acting as a 'relay-station', in Von der Leith's (1972a) term, transmitting messages from the rest of the family. This could be extended to include the outside world. We found this to be much rarer than anticipated, and less than that found by the Beattie (1981) study for instance. A child can take on the role of the 'relay-station' or the protector, encouraged by the hard-of-hearing parent or by a hearing parent wishing to transfer the role. Occasionally 'unsympathetic' spouses distanced

Figure 11.3 **Spectogram showing member of family acting as a relay station (2) for the hard-of-hearing person (1) to the rest of the family**

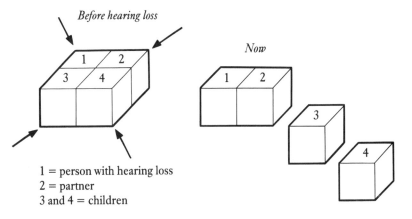

1 = person with hearing loss
2 = partner
3 and 4 = children

themselves from the hard-of-hearing partner by their own volition and by the presence of protective children. Six couples said 'it's us against the children'. Obviously there are many ways in which the family could align itself along the dimensions of protector and ally. One person said 'You need to be able to talk about it. ... I hope one day it will change though ... instead of me sort of reaching out for help from them, I wish they would come round' (37). (This man was referring here specifically to his children.)

Another pattern reported was for this mediating role to be seen as subverting the balance of power within the family. One man said 'We are completely equal except when she talks for me' as though he then lost his equal standing and became inferior. Figure 11.4 shows a pattern when a change was seen as a complete reversal of power because of this. The man in Figure 11.4 said 'Before I had my hearing aid, she was my ears and took more control. I was on top before I lost my hearing, then afterwards, she was' (14). For him he found having a hearing aid had restored the status quo. It was an isolated example of such a clear-cut 'control' division.

Figure 11.4   Spectogram showing change of 'control' within a family

Before hearing loss

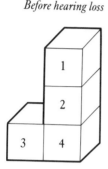

Now

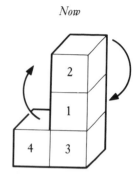

1 = person with hearing loss
2 = partner
3 and 4 = children

This element of control of information is something which we developed as a model to use in this research. In the case of acquired hearing loss, increased vulnerability occurs and the person may struggle to regain mastery as part of the adaptation. Steering a path between independence and dependence, over-support and protection, is a difficult one, and one which requires us to understand the position of the 'important others'.

INTIMACY

Intimacy is to some extent a concept determined by individual differences. It is likely to be multi-faceted but it is a concept at the heart of personal relations. Intimacy in the home draws on previous shared experiences as well as on existing routines and the present state of the relationship. Couples may have strong bonds because of this shared background and the ease with which it can be invoked to negotiate the meaning of current situations. Obviously a major element in this is ease of communication. Disturbing this alters not the past but the

188

capacity to invoke it; in doing this it directly affects people's closeness and ability to negotiate about current happenings. Our study showed that the way in which the level of intimacy was affected was in particular through the loss of intimate talk. This applied to both hearing and hearing-impaired people and affected both physical and emotional intimacy. One hearing husband said, 'Bedtime is strictly limited now, I can't ever whisper sweet nothings to her now' (27). Another hearing wife said, 'What I find is I miss the quiet chats at night, in bed. I think of something and I don't tell him because of the effort involved in getting out of bed and getting his hearing aid on' (39). Taking out aids at night involved problems with children waking as well as feelings of inadequacy about hearing burglars or babies. Others mentioned the noise hearing aids made if anyone came close, which proved an embarrassment in some situations. This was given as another reason for taking hearing aids out in bed (the first being discomfort). For couples with children, the time alone for talk either had to be regulated into 'formal' talks for important issues or, at the other extreme, one couple who said, 'We just don't talk any more' (1). Measuring the 'effort' involved in conversation was frequently mentioned. This was either from the hearing person's point of view in explaining things, jokes especially, or comments thought to be *not worth the effort*. Matched by this was the hearing-impaired person's perceptions of some conversations at mealtimes where there was more than one hearing person, it was often described as simply 'not worth the effort' to keep up. This was an area where relationships seemed particularly vulnerable.

CONTROL

We have considered control elsewhere in terms of adjustment and other researchers have used power and independence as ways of describing the same phenomenon. It is difficult to define within relationships since it is an attempt to describe the underlying dynamic of that relationship. In any group a leader might be expected to emerge, but in the case of 'family' the notion of leader is too simple. Members of a unit may be seen as part of a constantly changing unit, or at least of a unit with the capacity for change. Within that framework control has to be seen as taken and given by different people within the unit at different times. The word control may not have been the one used by the informants.

189

However, in seven spectograms putting one member 'on top' was spontaneously used. One hearing-impaired man, after rearranging the blocks into a close family, saw this very clearly as an example of control – he described it as 'they will change to accommodate my needs' (58). He was referring to a time when his hearing declined further and a change in behaviour was required.

Contrasting with this is the view taken by the hearing-impaired man who saw his hearing loss as accompanied by a complete loss of control, saying 'Now I'm at the bottom of the pile, before I was on top' (15). For this man his hearing impairment had also meant the loss of a job as a skilled baker which he had held for fifteen years. He was dismissed for a seemingly meaningless reason of 'infection' because he had suffered a mastoid years before. The perceived injustice had led to increasing depression and inability to cope with his hearing loss. By the second interview he had changed from initial optimism with his hearing aid restoring his position as head of the family to an extreme view of himself as right at the bottom. His wife did not agree with that view of the family at all and saw him as still the 'head of the family'. Loss of work and hearing combined to alter totally his view of himself within the family making him feel completely worthless. Asked about the future, he said, 'I'll be six foot under' and could not anticipate any future at all. Asked why, he said he had a number of 'complaints' (none of which were terminal).

This is a rather extreme example and although it is in a sense 'classic', we found the type rather rare. The spectograms therefore tell us about family structure but require us to infer from the transcribed interviews more on the power structure within the family. Does this mean for example that in 'traditional' families with a male head of household that the rest of the family will rearrange itself to accommodate his needs more readily than if it is the female partner who loses her hearing. It is worthy of note here that women received far less encouragement than men to wear their hearing aids as well as reporting that they felt they received less understanding. Are the family less likely to change to accommodate the demands of a female member's hearing loss and is this affected by the economic role of the woman in that household? The other question raised is whether or not the children change more than the husband in this type of family situation. There are a number of issues raised here which offer valuable insights into how elements such as power and control within relationships directly affect adaptation to hearing loss.

CHILDREN

A particular area of difficulty was found to be relations with children. Beattie (1981) claimed that teenagers and daughters of all ages emerged as particularly difficult for the hearing-impaired person. An element here may be the point Beattie made that any hearing-impaired adult living with *two or more hearing adults* experiences handicap or isolation, because there are other high-level conversations from which they are excluded. Some people in our study reported teenagers as difficult but how this is to be separated from 'normal' difficult adolescent behaviour it is hard to say.

Babies and young children waking at night was reported as an area where conflict could arise; deciding which partner in the family has to attend to the children at 3am is always difficult. If one partner is hearing-impaired it creates additional strain. The pattern in Figure 11.5 is indicative of this situation. The children (both under 2 years old) were seen as a barrier between the partners as a result of the wife's loss of hearing. The wife felt that in the maternity hospital she had already been labelled as an 'inadequate mother' when the nurses took away her baby at night, 'because I couldn't hear it' (27). By the time she came home she already felt she was not coping with the baby, so her husband had taken over the baby's night-time feeds completely,

Figure 11.5 Spectogram of family showing children seen as barrier because of the hearing loss

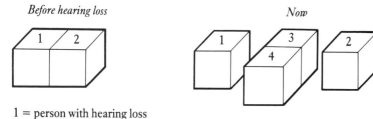

Before hearing loss   *Now*

1 = person with hearing loss
2 = partner
3 and 4 = children

191

and it had consequently become a source of resentment for him and inadequacy for her.

CONCLUSION

The spectograms then illustrate some useful areas for looking at changes in relationships because of hearing loss. Control in relationships is significant where people feel loss of independence is synonomous with loss of control. Competing needs within relationships is another area to focus upon – where there are children their presence can be negative when their demands cut across the needs of the parents; however, as 'relay stations' they can be supportive within the family. There is also evidence of the drawing together of families after a hearing loss into an equidistant close group. Relationships were seen as showing some interesting and unexpected changes after hearing loss which leads us to think there is a great deal of scope there for further work.

12

Hearing loss – a deafened perspective*

Ten years ago, it would have been inconceivable that this book would have been written and that a person with a profound hearing loss should be part of the research team. What has changed most in the intervening decade is the conception of illness, disease, and disability. The new 'holistic' view of the person as a totality implies that a malfunction in one part of the system, be it psychological or physical, has implications for the well-being of the rest. The process works in both directions so that just as the physical has implications for the psychological equilibrium of a person, so emotional trauma has in its own way physical implications. With an acquired hearing loss the holistic approach can be used although it is complex. The medical approach, quite naturally, has concentrated almost exclusively on restoring hearing, either by way of surgical intervention or by the issuing of a hearing aid. As surgical techniques become even more sophisticated and advances in microelectronics filter through to hearing-aid development, the approach does help people. Even profound hearing loss in certain special cases may respond to cochlear implants. Yet for those who have cared to examine the testimony of people in the past, especially the well known and famous, and the contemporary magazines for the hard-of-hearing and deaf, more than ample indications exist that not all is well.

What often emerges is a story of frustration, anger, and emotional stress that leaves many of the hearing-impaired with an intense feeling that very few hearing people understand their experience. But for the person going progressively deaf, and especially for those who become profoundly deafened in a short space of time through accident or

* This chapter has been written by Peter Wood, himself deafened at 32 years of age.

illness, there is no counselling. To whom do they express their fears and hopes? Not everyone can express the sense of hopelessness that they may feel as they rightly or wrongly perceive that their families are not only unsympathetic but in addition are shunning them. How are the families of those people expected to cope with a situation in which no guidelines have been available. Those which now exist are based on limited research. Yet they have a lot to say, these deaf and hard-of-hearing people. They know that they have a problem and that all is not well either with themselves, or with their relationships with others. The onus is therefore on the professionals involved with hearing loss to find out what people have experienced, how they cope, why they fail to cope, and what can be done to remedy this in the future.

It is necessary to declare my interest and perhaps motivation, at this stage. As a profoundly deafened person for sixteen years and a member of the research team, I often found myself in an ambiguous and confusing situation. The ambiguity arose because I was attempting to examine objectively a phenomenon or experience that is also personal.

In my own case, hearing declined from normal to a profound loss in the space of several weeks and resulted in immediate hospitalization in what turned out to be a vain attempt to halt any further decline. The sense of immediate shock at being totally deaf was further compounded by the unfamiliar surroundings in which I found myself. The immediate and pressing need to know what was happening was frustrated by an almost total lack of communication. Subsequently it was seen as simply the case that the consultant staff did not know the cause of my deafness but were either unwilling or unable to be so frank. It may have been that this was considered in the interests of the patient but it merely compounded anxiety.

At this stage, the deafened person has a turmoil of feelings, but for me bafflement and confusion bordering on panic dominated, to be replaced by spells of emotional numbness. A final meeting with the consultant gave me very little additional insight, only the advice to contact the local deaf centre who he believed might possibly help. The initial panic and turmoil gave way to some thoughts for the future. It is incredibly difficult to accept that one can hear nothing, and even more difficult then and now to accept that this silence will continue into the future. There is a tendency to believe that the loss is temporary only and will somehow return. This self-delusion is not confined to sudden deafness as I well know but is an attempt to reject and ignore threats to one's well-being and self-image. In addition, one does not feel 'deaf', just a hearing person cut off from sound as if the world is viewed through a soundproof window.

Until my discharge from hospital I had given little thought to the future and a warning of potential problems only arose when several colleagues from the office paid a visit. I immediately sensed the acute embarrassment they were undoubtedly undergoing. People with whom one could and did relax and joke now suddenly wished to terminate the rudimentary and basic conversation with notepad and pen as soon as possible. This was the first assault as such on my sense of self-identity, a glimpse that others would no longer see and accept me as I was and as I had previously been. One felt like protesting to them 'look it's still me, only my ears have packed up, you know, not my brain'.

A number of priorities emerged at this point. Firstly how to cope with the deafness; the problem of employment where communication was vital; and the implications for the future. A visit to the local 'deaf institute', as it then was, created a sense of profound depression. Like so many of the deaf centres and clubs that existed in a network throughout the UK my own local centre had been established in the late nineteenth century by church ministers with funding provided by local businessmen. The aim was mainly pastoral rather than the development of the older deaf person in order that they could achieve their full potential as human beings; nor was it concerned with the rehabilitation of those with an acquired hearing loss. The aim was religious and most specifically evangelical and a continuation of school; hence the use in their descriptions of 'missioner' or 'mission to the deaf'.

Participants were seen as being dependent on the hearing staff and neither played, nor were allowed to play, any role in the management of their own affairs. Things have changed somewhat over the past decade but the ethos of dependency still lingers in many ways. To a formerly hearing person who had enjoyed a large measure of autonomy and held a responsible position in a large company, it came as a shock. The prospect of acquiring sign language held little appeal, in fact was viewed with a certain horror. It was and still is equated with dumbness in many people's mind and dumbness equated with deficient intellect. But in addition the system seemed at first alien, and only serving to draw the attention of others to one's deafness. I attended lip-reading classes and like so many others before me found reciting proverbs and simple sentences easy enough in the artificial confines of a weekly group. But when attempting to apply lip-reading outside the group, it seemed like a cruel hoax. Comprehension ranged from limited to absolutely nothing. Recourse to a pen and notepad became the usual, in fact only, effective means for others to communicate with me. Unemployment rapidly loomed as a major concern. Not being able to cope with the demands of the previous job as a project administrator in Aerospace – in fact not even being allowed to try to cope – the alternatives were either non-existent or as I perceived it an insult to my pride and intelligence. It was rapidly brought home to me how utterly dependent modern society is on communication.

As the months went by and became years, so too did a measure of insight emerge. I met through the local hard-of-hearing club a wide range of members but their advice and experiences only drew attention to the gap that separated us. In the case of the deafened, the hearing loss usually develops over a short space of time, such as days or weeks, usually as the result of accident or illness. This creates an immediate trauma psychologically, within the family, vocationally, and socially. There is, as I found, no possibility of the person still being accepted by others as they were in the past. Communication becomes either impossible or laboriously slow, by means of a notepad and pen. Conversation, with all its nuances and irony effectively stopped for me on the day I became deaf. The inability to communicate effectively produces frustration and bitterness. Even now, some sixteen years later, hardly a week goes by without some reminder of what has been lost. Even such things as a railway station announcement or being unable to return the conversation of a fellow passenger on a train produces a tension. As one's social circle, if not declining, becomes more restricted to those who one knows, it is nevertheless faced with the impact of frustration. Sometimes in these circumstances there emerges the feeling of being an outsider in one's dealings with the rest of society so that our presence becomes a physical rather than participatory one: dependant on others to find out what is said or happening rather than being a contributor.

There is a tendency, indeed attraction, in these circumstances to become introverted and subjective. Just as Beethoven claimed that the only time he could ignore his deafness was when he was composing music, so the deafened if intellectually inclined realize the world of the imagination still exists for them. For myself, it has been to a large extent my safety net. Whether or not others feel this inward withdrawal as a positive response to deafness is of little concern. It has provided a new authenticity in my life and that is all that matters.

I am often asked by colleagues, friends, and other researchers into

196

deafness how much have I changed as a result of becoming deafened, and how it has affected my outlook. The effect has been profound I believe. Like other deafened people, the bitterness and frustration gave way to a sense of dissonance and tension. At first there exists the feeling that, apart from the problem of a hearing loss, we are the same and in no way changed. We want to carry on as before, with others making allowances for our deafness. It is not just that other people will not always accept us on our chosen terms, but a realization that it is unrealistic for them to do so. Whilst I personally rebelled against the notion that we are simply what environmental and social forces make us, I was nevertheless gradually forced to accept that we are an integral part of a community and that community possesses norms and values. I was therefore forced to accept that at best a synthesis could be achieved in which, whilst I could not always manage to get society to accept me as I was, I would not on the other hand be forced into a 'deaf role' or 'deaf ghetto'. In this respect, the militant campaigns of the signing community have been of immense, if indirect, help. Subtle and gradual changes also occur in basic beliefs, in the cultural, religious, and political. It is far more complex than just a cause and effect. It is not that previously one saw the world as a person with normal hearing but now through the eyes of the deafened. The experience leads to reflection and a subsequent reappraisal and, occasionally, rejection of formerly held beliefs. It has changed relationships with others beyond recognition. Interaction requires now a specific effort on their behalf. Those who under the circumstances of normal hearing would have provided polite but essentially meaningless conversation now no longer bother. Avoidance by former friends has remained encouragingly low. New situations are approached with trepidation and I have yet to achieve the difficult tactical knack of knowing when to tell another person that I am totally deaf.

At this point, it must be fairly obvious that I came to the project with a whole matrix of experiences and views. We hoped that my experiences would encourage candour in our participants. Experience showed that there would be a greater tendency to confide. The decision to concentrate on the family, as being a catalyst in the whole adjustment process, has been set out earlier in the book. My own view regarding this in the planning stage was one of total agreement. Having had no one else to turn to during the literally awful initial stages of deafness, I was only too well aware of the enormous burden other members of the family must bear. There are few other opportunities provided by society to express one's bitterness, frustration, hopes, and fears. The tragedy is compounded in that they, as much as the deafened person, have little knowledge of how to cope with the traumatic experiences they have to share. To expect that this process should occur in isolation without any real support or advice is beyond belief. But this has happened in the past again and again whenever a person has become deafened or hard-of-hearing.

Gradually, as a result of these insights, there developed the view that adjustment was not a once-and-for-all event in time but a continuous process, and one that might still be occuring several decades after the onset of a loss. We were also aware from the interviews we had carried out on previous projects that to consider this process as beginning from the point at which a hearing loss was officially diagnosed was unrealistic. It was felt that a single point of onset was to all intents indeterminable. Change in life circumstances like the ageing process is not detectable on a day-by-day or even monthly basis. Most people appear to live within the specific and the present rather than continually indulging in a comparative analysis of the present with the past and a potential future. Even amongst the deafened where the hearing loss is total on a once-and-for-all basis, adjustment is difficult to define even over long periods. Yet it undoubtedly occurs. At times it appeared that we were seeking the impossible in that we expected participants to articulate emotional and relationship changes of which they were at best only vaguely conscious. There may be a difference here between the hard-of-hearing and the deafened. The deafened face immediate trauma so that anything from that point on can only be an improvement. The hard-of-hearing often fact a continuing decline so that the outlook is seen as progressively bleaker. Unfortunately, we did not have contact with a sufficient number of profoundly deafened to consider this point. Contact with organizations such as the National Association of Deafened People suggests the possibility of this being so. It was surprising to find that not only did the hard-of-hearing retain their hearing outlook but many moved even further away from adopting any sense of deaf identity. The importance of this finding for those concerned with rehabilitation facilities cannot be overstated.

The changes in family relationship was also found to be far more extensive and subtle than the writer anticipated. With the hard-of-hearing it was envisaged that roles and interaction would not change so much. However the sense of being left out was expressed by many as being of real concern. Associated with this problem of being present but not participating was the almost naive faith that other family members placed on hearing aids. Few seemed to realize the limitations that arise in their use. The difficulty with children, especially teenagers, was difficult to separate from the normal developmental problems of this age range and experience with the deafened throws little additional light on this area. The writer feels that this exclusion is not in most cases a deliberate act or a conscious one, but rather a lack of sympathetic identity.

When developing the concepts that allowed the creation of our 'model of phases', we were forced to deal with the ambiguities that had arisen. It was difficult for the research team to accept the views of past researchers such as Orlans (1985) that in the final analysis adjustment is determined by the individual. It simply did not fit current concepts and theories concerning the family, health, and caring. Neither did it fit with the massive increase in supportive social services. The writer has given much thought to this and cannot claim that either approach fully satisfied intellectually. A clue may be derived from the massive number of variables identified that affects the outcome of a hearing loss, psychologically, socially, vocationally. This should, I believe, warn us of developing too reductionist an approach, in seeing the problem of deafness as being 'nothing but' a malfunction of the ear; 'nothing but' a psychological problem; 'nothing but' a family interaction problem. It is of course all of those things. We need to recognize the immense complexity of that adjustment but this will only be of lasting value if the professionals working with the hard-of-hearing and deafened can also do so. We have seen how the deafened and hard-of-hearing refuse to be labelled and refuse to adopt an identity of deafness despite pressure from society to do this. The extent to which this refusal to become what others would wish them to become leads to frustration, bitterness, and isolation, or to a new and valid role for the future at home, within the family, and with the rest of society should be the concern of us all.

DEAFENED PEOPLE IN RESEARCH

It is one thing, however, to agree in principle that the deafened or hard-of-hearing should take part in research but the problems of them doing so must be faced. The easy option of confining them to the office where they could undoubtedly perform many of the routine project tasks should be avoided, as it does not face up to the problem of participation. This approach was tried in the past not only with the deafened but also the pre-lingually deaf who were advised to take up jobs not involving communication. The problem is that almost all social science research is based on eliciting information from participants; communication is therefore essential.

Our earlier research overcame the problem by using an almost exclusively questionnaire-based personal interview format. This proved effective in that the nature of the information we sought – mainly straightforward facts such as 'how long have you possessed a hearing aid?' – could easily be elicited. Additional comments from participants were obtained by open conversation after completion of the questionnaire. The interview took place at the university in a room where only the deafened researcher and the hard-of-hearing participant was present. Distractions were therefore reduced to an absolute minimum. Even so the problem rapidly became apparent. The deafened find other deafened or hard-of-hearing no easier to comprehend than hearing people. The limitations of lip-reading have already been pointed out. Interviewing therefore became a laborious and slow process. As the majority were hard-of-hearing and found a hearing aid effective the communication problem was mainly centred on myself. As the open-ended conversation part of the interview was mainly to provide a background picture to the questionnaire data, it was possible to cope. It was when we approached the study of the family that greater difficulties emerged.

It was obvious at the planning stage of the project that a strictly questionnaire-based approach would be ineffective. The intricate interaction and changes in family relationships cannot be confined to such a restricted format; although we hoped to obtain a considerable amount of data in this way, much would depend on communication in the form of open discussion. Two other factors were involved in that apart from the hard-of-hearing subject there would also be a spouse present and a hearing researcher taking part. In addition the interview would take place in the family home with all the distractions that this entailed including others present, family pets, and unfamiliar surroundings. It was envisaged that the deafened researcher should interview the participant with the hearing loss whilst the hearing researcher should do likewise with the hearing partner. All four would then discuss family changes in open discussion including the use of wooden building blocks to provide data for spectographic analysis – outlined earlier. I have given much thought to the effectiveness of this approach as it obviously has profound implications for future deaf researchers, or more precisely those who are hard-of-hearing or deafened.

Whereas the prelingually deaf members of the signing community would appear to experience little difficulty in carrying out research amongst their own community, the hard-of-hearing researcher's effectiveness would depend on the level of residual hearing that they possessed and the benefit that they derived from a hearing aid. The deafened, however, in the framework of a multiple-participant interview, are faced with an almost impossible barrier. My own experience showed that the initial part of the interview with the hearing-impaired person which was on a one-to-one basis and mainly centred on the completion of a questionnaire was reasonably straightforward to complete. It was the open group discussion however that left me completely stranded, physically present but not participating. Constant attempts to include me in the discussion were made both by the hearing researcher and by the participants but it was a deliberate act that could easily break the flow of easy conversation. Only when we dealt with profoundly deaf participants did the nature of the interaction change so that once again I began to participate.

We attempted to overcome this problem by tape-recording the open discussion and obtaining transcripts, to be used both by myself and for further analysis. This provided much important data from the interview that I had missed. But even this, while perfectly adequate for the hearing researcher who had been present, was less satisfactory for me. As with reading the transcript of a play the words are physically present but what is lacking is the additional nuances and characterization. My own experiences with notepad and pen has given often embarrassing insights into how easy it is to misinterpret written communication and how easy irony, for instance, can be missed.

In addition the stress of coping with an interview in the family home is far greater than in the controlled surroundings of a room at the university. The desperate attempt to lip-read produces rapid fatigue in a deafened researcher and an hour appears the maximum tolerable. This obviously slows down the rate at which interviews can be held.

In a very real sense the problem of deafened researchers taking part in a project of this nature is the problem of being deafened itself. Nearly all the problems they face are present throughout the project not just in the interviews. This I believe brings home to hearing researchers on the project the problems that they are dealing with. Ivory-tower 'objectivity' becomes impossible in such circumstances. Overall the presence of a deafened researcher is I believe not only beneficial but probably essential. In dealing with acquired hearing loss where the implications are to a large extent subjective and psychological, the insights of the deafened coupled with the most objective approach of the hearing researchers provide the degree of insight and understanding that has not in the past been available.

IV

Putting it all together

13

In search of a model

It is inevitable on reaching this stage of a study that the researchers can be seen standing with armfuls of data and findings and no bags to put them in. The sheer weight of results and the variety and unevenness of the patterns are very daunting indeed. Hearing-loss work is just like this and it is easy to see why writers have in the past given up with statements on the complexity or the singularity of acquired hearing loss: 'But in the final analysis, the task of adjustment, of living with the disability, is up to the individual' (Orlans 1985: 192).

Orlans chooses to finish on a positive note in his analysis but there is a sense of resignation about the view that 'he's still the same person; he's just gone deaf'. Our results and the views of countless autobiographies indicate that hearing-impaired people do *not* feel they are the same. In our study the people who feel they are unchanged tend to be those who are not diagnosed. Perhaps they have not been resocialized into being hard-of-hearing. We do not wish to defend this last point just yet but hearing loss requires a better presentation than it has had so far. We can no longer accept that 'in the end it's the individual' as the only explanation, in view of the recent work not only on family systems but also interaction and illness behaviour. We have tried to present a framework of this theory and background research, we have presented our data as simply as possible, and we have offered a model of the temporal process in hearing loss; it is now time to try to put it all together in a model which will tell us about hearing loss.

In an ideal world the model would be simple, the Ohms law of hearing loss, or at least it would be mathematically specificable, such as the planetary system in our solar system. Unfortunately, our world is not ideal nor has any discipline yet been able to explain human behaviour in this prescriptive a fashion. Our model needs to be temporally valid. It has to be able to describe adequately the pattern of hearing-loss onset, treatment, and change. It ought to be predictive. That is, it should tell us that given a series of influences individuals are more likely to experience life in this way. It will be probabilistic in that it will suggest the likelihood of events rather than the certainty. Finally, the model must be consistent with other views of families and individuals, societies and disability. In doing this it can be more effectively understood and applied. This chapter is a first or second approximation to this. We believe the model is temporally valid and consistent with other theories outside hearing loss research (though not necessarily consistent with those within). Whether it is predictive or even useful in anticipating hearing-loss problems requires time and continued testing.

We need to set out some technical but basic concepts, to examine some of the factors which we believe to be relevant, and then to present a final framework.

SOME BASIC FEATURES

When reading the literature and examining previous research it is easy to summarize the effects of acquired hearing loss. *It makes people neurotic*; that is anxious, insecure, likely to behave differently. Yet these are descriptions of the individual in conjunction with the environment and the two cannot be separated. These descriptions are not symptoms but responses. They are descriptions of disturbance in the social world.

Therefore, in rejecting this explanation of hearing loss, i.e. that it makes people neurotic, and its remedy through counselling of the hearing-impaired, we are pointing not to its wrongness but to its incompleteness. To understand deaf people or hard-of-hearing people we must incorporate as much of the interpersonal relationship as is possible. To do so will be to offer a completely different framework for counselling from that which the western medical framework has so far provided.

We offer a number of simplifying concepts:

1 The *progress of hearing loss* is the temporal dimension in which hearing loss occurs. People acquire a loss gradually or suddenly, respond to it, and live with it.

2 The individual participates in an informational exchange throughout social life. The extent of the exchange is determined by the

individual's *control* and the extent to which society is perceived as controlling the exchanges.

3 Hearing loss disturbs the information exchange to an extent determined by the interaction of *life factors* and creates further threats to control in the form of *resultant* factors.

4 *Life factors* may be *fixed, socially determined,* or *controllable* by the individual.

5 Life factors taken together are the life-state of the individual.

6 *Resultant factors* in hearing loss are generally *negative* from a societal view but need not be from an individual's view.

7 *Adjustment* occurs at any time and over time in the progress of hearing loss when the balance of these factors presents a reduction in stress for the interactants and the environment.

8 Stress occurs when the requirements for control and exchange of information cannot be met in the situation or by the interactants.

9 Adjustment is likely to be seen when:
 (a) the level of control by the individual or by society is altered;
 (b) the exchange of information is enhanced;
 (c) the interactants in negotiation either implicitly or explicitly seek to alter (a) or (b).

In simpler terms, people acquire hearing loss during a period in their lives when varying factors influence their daily lives. The extent of the hearing loss affects their likelihood of continuing as before in relation to its extent and the factors of personal position, social interaction, and social custom. The most likely initial result is personal and social stress, particularly in the 'family'. The individual with varying speed will begin to experience diminished ability to regulate interaction and may find the position in relations at home and in society threatened.

To 'adjust', the demands on social interaction and the demands of society on the individual must be brought into a balanced state whereby there is less stress in the environment.

Perhaps the process can best be described in terms of the progress of hearing loss. In Figure 4.4 there were four phases: normal hearing, hearing loss, hearing loss recognition, adjustment. We have already considered these temporal phases in Chapter 4. At this point it is appropriate therefore to tackle a second aspect, the factors in the individual's life-state which relate to hearing loss.

FACTORS INFLUENCING THE PARTICIPANTS IN HEARING LOSS

A wide range of influences go to make up each individual and each interaction that individual engages in. We believe that there are significant factors at work throughout the individual's life which determine the view of the world adopted, the self-image, and the actual family relation occurring. Despite their importance, not all of these come into play in the hearing-loss situation. Our research findings offer slightly different determining factors and also suggest that some general life factors are not directly related to adaptation to hearing loss despite being important in understanding the individual. We need to describe the general factors first.

Family stage

By this we mean the marital and home situation reached by the individual. It is primarily social and normative. Many people have an expectation to move from adolescence to marriage to having children to middle age to retirement. Our social expectations are built-in early and are very durable. The fact that these patterns are no longer strictly adhered to lessens the stress experienced for those not meeting these 'requirements'. However, getting older often takes these stages for granted. Disruption of a person's functioning will have different meaning at each stage. Society and the media commonly portray accidents as disaster when they occur when there are dependent children; most seriously when it is the 'head of household' who has the accident.

Work status

Similarly work has been an expectation of our society for a long time although again this is no longer the only pattern. Unemployment and part-time work are more common. Disability affects functioning in the work setting and traditionally the individual has to accept the responsibility for the problem.

Socioeconomic status

This clearly relates to the first two factors though it is not determined by them. Financial effectiveness may well provide a solid basis for support when hearing loss occurs. At the same time social position may bring its own status. We do not feel this is an easy factor to interpret in relation to hearing loss.

The list of these general factors could go on almost endlessly. They are the factors which go towards making the individual in the environment. We have considered other general factors and find them not to be directly relevant or predictive of outcomes in our study. These include sex of the person (though there may be a link to position within the family), education level (there is no direct link to level of education reached though it should be said it is difficult to find an adequate criterion for education in this age group), recency since hearing-aid issue (again this arises because difficulties in establishing meaningful criteria – some people with recent aids have had hearing losses for a very long time – mean that our analysis will ultimately have to use the phases described earlier).

There is a series of factors which do seem to relate to hearing loss adjustment in a more direct way. Health is one, self-image and communicative relations at home are further examples.

Health

General physical functioning clearly affects one's ability to cope with problems. On the one hand it has set up an expectation for normal bodily function and participation in life. Sudden hearing loss will require the person to re-examine the level of medical well-being. In this sense good health followed by sudden disability may create wholly negative feelings about hearing loss and make it much more difficult to adapt. Gradual onset, however, as we have discovered, offers the chance to adjust. The better the individual's health the more easily the implications of hearing loss will be examined and the more likely will be the unconscious adjustment.

However, health problems after hearing loss also create difficulties; but when they are serious they may act to take the pain out of hearing loss by making it subsidiary to the main problem.

Eighteen people from the diagnosed group of ninety-four mentioned other health problems as being significant. Only one of the pre-diagnostic group (a man who had had one lung removed and was in receipt of invalidity benefit) saw his state of health as an issue. These are summarized in Table 13.1. The effects of health must be distinguished as:

Table 13.1   Other health problems

Colostomy	1	
Mastectomy	1	
Heart attack	4	
Epilepsy	1	
Diabetes	1	
Psoriasis	1	
Chronic bronchitis	1	
Visual handicap	3	
Brain tumour	1	
Disease of central nervous system	3	
Unspecified surgery	1	
	18	of diagnosed group of 94
One lung removed	1	of undiagnosed group of 29

Note: Four of the hearing members of households had a mental handicap and one had spina bifida.

(i) those which were directly related to the hearing loss, e.g. whiplash fractures after road accidents which involved a risk of paralysis and further injury;

(ii) those which were current health problems at the time of interview, e.g. psoriasis; and

(iii) a previous illness which made the hearing loss seem of less importance by comparison, e.g. a mastectomy two years previously.

Health may be a positive factor for some respondents where a life-threatening illness makes the hearing loss seem mild by comparison to both the hard-of-hearing and hearing partners. One man said, after his wife had been diagnosed as having cancer and underwent surgery, 'I've taken on a different role since the operation. I take more care now. I'm more understanding about the hearing since, I've got it in perspective. I used to go out all the time' (74).

For other people, though, a chronic illness just added to the general feeling of helplessness. One man who had diabetes and psoriasis, and was taking anti-depressants, said 'It's always something, one thing seems to clear up and something else, like the diabetes, comes along – it's one thing on top of another ... all the other complaints get built up.' Asked how hearing loss affected his life he said 'I think it must have clamped it down a bit because I never used to go to parties or go out because of the psoriasis and the hearing problem ... if I never had the psoriasis perhaps I would have gone out more, but seeing I had that *and* the deafness, I just didn't go out much' (15).

There is no simple connection between other complaints and hearing loss; for some it is an additional problem to contend with which depresses them, for others it is something that makes it seem bearable.

Another woman with epilepsy said she wouldn't wear a hearing aid 'because I can't wear a hearing aid and be epileptic ... it made another affliction, you know' (26). She felt the epilepsy was worse than the hearing loss though, because of medication and people's reaction (although that was sometimes nearly as bad about hearing loss, she said). However, the two together meant she felt she was more of a 'burden'. If she didn't hear the phone her daughter worried. 'It wouldn't have been such a burden if I hadn't been epileptic – the two together made it worse because what did she [the daughter] think – "she's had a fit".' What makes the difference is obviously partly other people's reaction to the illness. Both these two people mentioned other people's responses.

One person's situation is worth looking at in detail, to illustrate a number of points about the relationship of health and hearing. A man in his 40s, with a heart complaint, at the first interview said he felt that his hearing was nothing compared to his heart problems – both had occurred one month before the first interview and his hearing was at that time much improved after a sudden dramatic loss whilst in hospital following a heart attack. However, one year later when his hearing was still at the same level as at the first interview and his heart condition was unchanged, he said he felt they were 'about the same' as disabilities. 'Heart-wise, I can't go for a long walk or walk up hills or anything like that, with hearing it's things like you can't hold a conversation in the pub or at work. ... If I'd stayed as deaf as I was in hospital, it would have been a bigger problem than my heart, actually, from a social point of view' (17). So, weighing up other health factors is part of the process for this man of his adjusting to a hearing loss. For him, both his problems were of an uncertain nature which he felt could become worse at any time – which obviously added to a feeling of tension. However, despite feeling a strong sense that he was 'inferior' and that 'disability in our society made us to be looked down upon as

211

inferior', he seemed to manage well and not be unduly concerned about his health problems, saying that the thing to do was to find other interests, which he felt he had. His health was affecting his work, where he was in danger of losing his job, having been moved to a lighter one after his heart attack. Because he did not hear instructions (he worked with lorries in a maintenance depot) he said that he realized he was a safety risk, but even this additional strain, because of his health, did not seem to unduly depress him. For his family, he and his wife both felt they had been drawn closer together by the experience of ill-health and adversity. His wife felt that his hearing was not nearly so bad for her to cope with as having nearly lost him, and she found the life-threatening nature of the heart attack problem far more worrying.

In this situation, hearing loss is understandably more easy to 'accept' and for this family simply less important in life. For them the change required by hearing loss was relatively minor. While his physical health had been affected an attitude which offered stability in mental health was vital.

Self-image

The importance of self image in adapting to a disability has often been stressed. It relates to our concepts of control and power and determines the individual's belief in the ability to influence events in the environment. It is a characteristic of the pre-diagnostic group who tend to reject hearing loss on one hand yet modify their behaviour and use positive strategies to counteract hearing loss. It may bring them into conflict of belief with partners as we have seen, but its preservation is vital to adequate adjustment.

Self-image is in some ways a catch-all concept at the present time. Nevertheless, it is sufficiently precise in the sense of the belief that the individual has of himself or herself in relation to events in the environment for us to consider it vital to understanding the process of adjustment. Perhaps we can best explain it in the context of one area: disclosure. This refers to the situation when the hearing-impaired person is supposed to own up to being deaf. It is a declaration to another or a group that there is a hearing problem, and we frequently consider adjustment related to an individual's confidence in this.

But we need to consider the individual and the view of the world he

212

or she wishes to hold. We particularly need to understand how they interpret others' views of the hearing-impaired person's position. Safilios-Rothschild (1981) talks about resocialization, i.e. learning to be disabled as others see them. We wish to propose that this is not always a good thing. Different attitudes to disclosure are illustrated by the following quotes:

A hard-of-hearing woman: 'My husband leaves it up to me whether or not I tell people and I don't unless I'm really in difficulty' (30).

The wife of a hard-of-hearing man: 'I get annoyed because he won't tell people and just carries on pretending he can hear – it puts me in a difficult position and in the end I just blurt it out, "he's deaf" – then he gets cross'.

Both women describe situations after diagnosis when the problem of disclosure may be more likely (because of the use of a hearing aid, for instance). There is a tendency to talk about getting the person to admit to being deaf to make things easier or avoid embarrassment, and yet the vast majority, from our research, refuse to disclose to strangers until, like the first woman above, they are in great difficulty.

Non-disclosure could be the strategy adopted by hearing-impaired people because:

(a) they do not believe they are deaf;
(b) they believe they have a hearing problem but encounter it only in certain environments, e.g. noisy pubs so there is no point in explaining it when it can be blamed on the environment;
(c) they believe they have a hearing problem but consciously or unconsciously believe that others are not able to adapt or understand and as a result would jeopardize either their status or their communication.

Despite the discomfort hearing viewers have experienced of the situation, we believe (c) is the most common. That is, adaptation may include being aware of hearing loss, i.e. one may need to know about hearing loss to deal with it, but that is rather different from telling people about it.

There is a tension created when non-disclosure occurs. There can be puzzlement and rejection by the hearing people who are strangers. For the partner who sees the confusion in the reaction of others there can be acute embarrassment. As a response, the hearing partner produces either covertly or overtly a disclosure to dissipate the tension. While this may provide an explanation to hearing people in the group, we would claim that it does nothing for the position of the deaf person. That is, it does not make hearing people more responsive and often will produce the 'Does he take sugar?' syndrome whereby the hearing-impaired person is by-passed in the conversation.

It seems certain that family adjustment is best either when feelings are discussed and perceptions are understood even if they are not shared. For some family arrangements certain degrees of sharing are more appropriate than others. However, we cannot assume that similarity of feeling means adjustment or 'coming to terms' with hearing loss. Indeed, it seems to be the opposite for those 'pre-diagnosed' people who express quite different views on the actual strategy used. These people are living with hearing loss much more effectively, judging by their lack of problems, than are those hearing-aid users. At the same time, we cannot assume that disclosure is a meaningful strategy until we have understood the self-image of the hearing-impaired person.

Family interaction

Adjustment is all about this shared understanding between partners or significant others and hearing loss as a disability is all about interaction whether in communication or perception. Reaching adjustment is not so much identifying in the individual the limitations but rather agreeing within the group how the group is affected. This is vitally important when we consider the family and home circumstances.

A final factor as a determinant of adjustment is the communicative links between the individual and the family. This cannot be simple since we start from a whole range of different positions as was shown by the spectograms in the previous chapter. The key is that satisfaction is expressed by the individual in relation to the level of communication now available. Family groupings may move together or apart in terms of empathy but as long as the communicative levels and the relevance of the information content are maintained, people in the family will express satisfaction. Where the meaning of events are not shared, where participation is difficult when the individual (hearing or hearing-impaired) seeks it, then change will be required.

This implies that not all adjustment will be towards greater participation but rather that it will be towards levels determined by other aspects of the individual's life state. So an introverted, non-dominant partner may withdraw more from group participation until the stress level is reduced and the communicative links are adequate, i.e. when what is said is understood by participants. Better communicative links and better strategies for communication (which will naturally exist in some families to a greater extent) will be able to maintain the level of interaction at a less-than-withdrawn level even where the hearing-impaired person is naturally introverted. In extroversion and high levels of self-image communication links may be more directly utilized by the hearing-impaired person again at an individually, situationally-based level.

Each factor contributes and is brought into play in different circumstances. To investigate them as a counseller requires an examination of the usual circumstances in which the individual finds himself or herself. It requires an examination of how partners contribute to the levels required and it requires an examination of how well resolved the differences in perception are in relation to dominance and control in the home.

There are further factors which are related to the hearing loss itself and to its outcomes which we have termed resultant factors. These include degree of the hearing loss (where not surprisingly we conclude that greater deafness makes the adjustment required rather greater); substitutions of activities (where for example group activity prior to loss can be substituted by paired or singular activity, e.g. by giving up football and playing golf; and features related to hearing loss such as tinnitus. Tinnitus presents problems of loss of sleep and lack of concentration, and does alter how the hearing loss is perceived. It is discussed at length in Chapter 6.

SUMMARY

It is in the end a vain hope that the jigsaw fits together well. It is at best a series of compromises because of our lack of knowledge of certain key areas such as family 'support' (and what it means) and the extent of normal communication at home. That is, we would need to carry out strict communication tasks with partners to establish how effectively they conveyed different types of information. We would also need an analysis of behaviour in the home. This might tell us exactly the way in which different relationships set their pattern of interaction and how successful it really seems to be.

We have put it all together in Figure 13.1. This complex picture of the individual is not prescriptive, i.e. we cannot list all the pro-factors

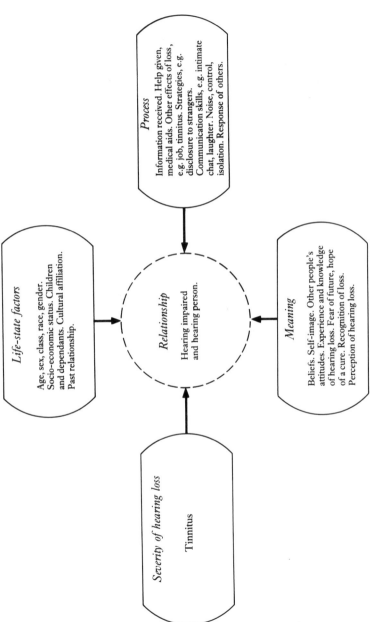

Figure 13.1 Influences on adapting in a relationship where one person has a hearing loss

and the con-factors and give a prescription to the relationship on how to adjust. At our present state of knowledge this is impossible. It could in future become feasible.

The main purpose of the figure is to highlight areas of concern for those tackling hearing loss in a counselling manner. Each aspect is vital to the picture of relationships and each scene produced, which can be described in terms of particular situations at home or outside, contributes to a more meaningful moving picture of the tasks required for adjustment. In Figure 13.2 we have the extension of the model begun in Chapter 4. It can only be considered a working model and we would expect it to change in time. It gives prominence to what we consider to be the key area prior to diagnosis when hearing loss is occurring without the understanding of the hearing participants. In phase 4 at least participants know a name for the problem and can act according to their knowledge and stereotypes. The extent to which the situations and relations are successful will depend on the characteristics of the individual and the type of relations which have existed in phase 2. We suspect problems in phase 2 may lead to breakdown in relations without there having been a complete understanding of the extent of the hearing loss. By the time the individual reaches phases 3 and 4 there may be a very weak communicative relationship and the scope for adjustment is correspondingly lessened.

The two figures offer different frameworks for dealing with people with hearing loss. Figure 13.1 emphasizes the factors and their inter-action suggesting that each situation the hearing impaired person experiences can be conceptualized in terms of these interacting forces. The student of hearing loss needs to map these interacting forces by investigation both formally and informally for any single relationship. The second figure offers a temporal overview of the progress of hearing loss and as such would be important in the planning of services and understanding the type of intervention possible at each time. Possibly one can begin to think about prevention in the sense of damaged relationships prior to phase 2.

This could occur in two ways. First, tactics for hearing could be made available to all people as a first step in taking away some of the fear and stigma of hearing loss. People could be led to expect poorer hearing in certain environments and greater difficulties in groups. Second, the whole idea of participants in hearing loss could be brought into play much earlier. People having difficulty communicating with (unknown to them) hearing-impaired people may be given information

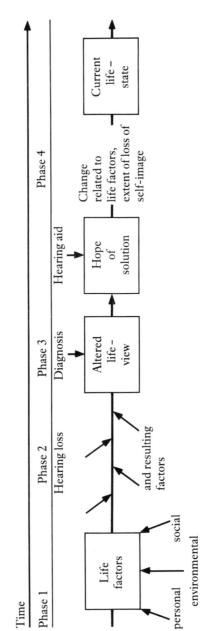

Figure 13.2 Extending the model in time as related to the events and factors

on the nature of hearing, its limitations, and the ideal circumstances for communication. It should not be considered a problem to adopt varying strategies for communication.

In phases 3 and 4 the picture changes as there is objective verification and labelling of hearing loss. It is here that Figures 13.1 and 13.2 can be combined to illustrate the full pattern of hearing-impairment and the relationships involved.

This whole model remains at an early stage. We believe it is a useful early stage. If it can be further examined in the light of data and practice in the field it may yield useful principles for approaching hearing loss.

14

Putting it all together

Becoming hearing-impaired in adult life produces a complex number of responses, both in the person concerned and in those with whom they share their life. To make this process easier, it is essential that we understand the nature of that process for participants. This book sets out to do that. The review of the literature reveals a major gap in the study of adjustment. Perhaps the interest shown in pre-lingual deafness in recent years may increasingly extend to acquired hearing loss but it has not done so yet. The growth in the number of elderly people in the population guarantees that in terms of service provision, the necessary skills and resources must be found to deal with elderly hearing loss at least. Whether or not this is extended to younger age groups remains to be seen. Whilst the majority of people who are hearing-impaired remain reluctant to be identified or to join together in order to try and change the situation, little is likely to be done to provide better services or improve hearing people's awareness of the problems. However, it is something that does affect so large a proportion of the population that it seems inevitable that the low-profile position of the hearing-impaired may change. This may not be in a highly visible 'militant' way, along the lines of some deaf groups, but there is evidence of this change developing. Ideas from other disabled groups and from recent work on disability has meant a change in attitude towards understanding disability as socially constructed. This means that the onus is more on hearing people to cope with the effects of hearing-impairment. The implications of this approach are an increase in practices not only at the level of individuals and the people they live with, but also at the wider level of providing 'deaf awareness' training for hearing people, both lay and professional. Hearing tactics for people with a hearing-impairment are another development which reflects this change in attitude. Increased awareness of the skills needed in order to participate fully in society means providing help given as 'hearing tactics' for people who are hearing-impaired. Assertiveness-training is another example of the same approach. People who are hearing-impaired could benefit from learning new skills to help make sure that their right to be included is put into practice.

Most of the people we talked to had mild hearing losses in the range averaging 36–52dB. Most people labelled themselves hard-of-hearing. They are an invisible group in many ways and mostly seem to prefer to stay that way. They discovered their hearing loss over time, in the main, and chose not to present themselves for diagnosis for a further few years. Most of the realization that there was a problem came from their asking for repetition or missing conversation at home. Interestingly these were situations where direct control cannot be used and the individual is forced to request help, i.e. repetition. Telephones and television were not perceived as such a problem by people with a hearing loss since control of volume could be affected either by adjusting the volume (television) or complaining of a bad line (telephone). People with more severe losses were more likely to avoid situations which highlighted their loss.

Referral emerged as a period of relief, in most cases a hope that something was being done or could be done. In contrast diagnosis was in itself often a traumatic experience negatively reported. The provision of a hearing aid produced more positive responses, perhaps because again 'something is being done'. The majority got help from hearing aids, though the confidence in adjustment was greater in those with mild losses. In fact those with mild losses tended to get the greatest understanding in diagnosis. Hearing partners had unrealistically high expectations of hearing aids and were reluctant to try them which may have contributed to their lack of understanding about the effects of wearing them.

There was a marked difference between the pre-diagnostic group and the diagnosed group. The pre-diagnostic group tended to be more positive and the partners tended to me more in tune than those who had been diagnosed. Hearing people were most affected by the noise level in the home, the area where the hearing-impaired person could exert most control. The television and radio were particularly difficult. Hearing members of the household complained constantly of the level of sound required by the hearing-impaired person.

Socially the pre-diagnostic group were more convinced that they made it obvious when they were not involved in conversation (although their partners tended to disagree with this). The diagnosed group were less likely to do this but more likely to sit passively pretending to follow. Does this imply a stronger self-image on the part of the pre-diagnosed group, a more positive attitude? The strategy of pretending to follow might seem rather a poor coping strategy but probably means a reduction in stress for the people with a hearing loss. Non-disclosure is perceived by some as a better strategy for this reason. It depends on the level of control available and the self-image of the hearing-impaired person.

Most of these conclusions come from the questionnaire responses. Change was reported to a significant degree in most areas, and decision-making, loss of intimacy, and talk were particularly noticed. Decision-making altered because of the loss of direct conversations and a change in power. On the whole people felt their adjustment had been good, but the majority did highlight changes in lifestyles and partners tended to underrate this change. Conversation did decline and there were differences in relation to children.

The return visits elicited a more negative and perhaps more realistic assessment. The general pattern indicates a slow development of negative reaction to the hearing loss diagnosis. A marked difference was noted in those who received help from their hearing aids by the second visit and expressed increased satisfaction.

The open-ended interview revealed a great deal about the quality of life for people with a hearing-impairment; in some cases there was isolation, embarrassment with strangers, and the constant attempt to hide the loss. The public world presented numerous difficulties through lack of understanding by hearing people and created the sheer exhaustion of trying to follow conversation. In private the problems concerned the decrease of intimate talk and joking and at certain ages contact with children became more difficult. People worked out re-sourceful ways of coping mostly on their own or with those close to them since there was little sign of any support from outside. Hardly anyone knew about environmental aids which would have overcome some of the major complaints from hearing partners about the level of noise in the home. The nature of hearing loss was interpreted by those experiencing it: some people saw it as a disability, others simply as a nuisance and their behaviour varied accordingly. There is a need to construct a more detailed picture of the perceptions of those who have

222

the hearing loss, about their own situation and what can be done to change it. The hearing partners also have a great deal to offer here in terms of their joint expertise and skills in interaction. The spectograms showed that it was possible for people to explain how they felt their hearing problem had changed their position in the family. For many the change had been for the worse towards a more isolated position for them.

There appears to be a pattern of phases as set out in the model in Chapter 13 that shows a marked negative evaluation of the situation beyond diagnosis. Most people interviewed were already developing adjustment before diagnosis. Predicting adjustment is more difficult. Two types of factors exist, those which arise from the person's own social situation influenced by, for example, race, gender, class, and age and those which result from the hearing loss. The latter include the extent of the loss, presence of tinnitus, sight problems in lip-reading, and the efficiency of any remedial help. It is the combination of these factors which influences the coping strategies.

If we were to draw out the implications for practice in hearing loss there would be a number of simple points. Coping strategies must be evaluated in the context of close relationships and social and economic position. Any mapping of an individual's need must take place within that context. Coping strategies occur long before referral to the hearing services; normally years before. As a result much of the research done comes years too late in the career of hearing-impairment. Research even at diagnosis occurs too late.

Coping strategies occur in a personal and social context and cannot be adequately dealt with if the services only provide auditory and technical advice and equipment. Counselling services are then seriously missing the mark if they concentrate on hearing-aid follow-up and do not work with relationships. There are major differences between those in the health system and those who have not reached referral. Both experience hearing loss and it remains to be examined whether the type of hearing loss in those in the pre-diagnostic stage is materially different, but the pre-diagnostic group show more positive responses and attitudes towards hearing loss and how it affects daily life. The progress of hearing loss can be divided into meaningful phases which indicate the state of the adjustment process. In many respects it would be helpful if counselling could be directed at phase 2 of hearing impairment in an attempt to prevent the arrival at phase 4 where attitudes appear to have hardened negatively, and where strategies adopted tend towards the passive and the isolationist patterns.

Assessment prior to counselling needs to take into account the broad range of variables which influence hearing-impairment. Life events, relationships, economic and social position, are all significant at this stage. To understand hearing loss adequately we need to use completed figures such as those proposed in Chapter 13. In this respect the resources available to hearing therapists seem totally inadequate. Hearing people are participants in hearing loss and need to be involved overtly in the adjustment process. Their involvement should occur as soon as hearing loss is suspected and this should not necessarily relate to hearing-aid provision. We can confirm a series of other points on hearing loss which have appeared in previous studies:

(a) it does not produce overall job loss;
(b) it does produce anxiety;
(c) it does affect control and interpersonal relations in the family;
(d) it tends to occur over a long period of time;
(e) it is usually mild in nature;
(f) it usually produces the identity 'hard-of-hearing'.

Change is perceived to happen in terms of lifestyle by most people. Real change in time tends to be towards more negative assessments of hearing loss. Hearing partners tend to overrate the success of hearing-aid use and underrate the lifestyle changes occurring. Frequent and significant differences in perception of hearing loss occur between partners. Given the dissatisfactions and misunderstandings, health workers at all levels should have some specific training in communicating with patients who are deaf or hard-of-hearing. It is also clear that information on environmental aids should be widely available.

Perhaps one of our most important points is that adjustment is change and this need not always be the change expected or desired by hearing participants or counsellors. It is still adjustment. Hearing-impaired people may find acceptance of hearing loss is vital to gradual adjustment but acceptance does not necessarily mean disclosure. The view that people should become confident about disclosure is not supported by our informants. The vast majority of hearing-impaired are not prepared to disclose hearing loss. Counselling or hearing therapy could take into account all of the factors involved in hearing loss: self-image, perceptions of hearing loss, significant relationships, and economic and social position of the person concerned. Working with the other members of the household should be an essential part of the process and would enhance the development of coping strategies.

Training in hearing tactics should be made widely available through adult education for friends and relatives as well as for anyone who is interested. 'Deaf awareness' courses could be adapted for use in institutions on a wide basis. Adult education might also be the appropriate setting for assertiveness-training and 'hearing tactics' for people who are hearing impaired.

Overall there are clear signs that people who acquire a hearing loss in adult life are an invisible group. They are partly invisible because for the most part they choose not to be noticed. However, this should not mean that their needs are not recognized. There are a number of ways that the services could be changed to make coping with a hearing loss easier. Attitudes towards disability in society generally are also important. Firstly in the sense that they influence how people interpret what is happening to them. Secondly in the way that disability is treated in our society. The change in emphasis towards people who are disabled themselves deciding what is best for them means that this group of people may be stranded between the more active groups demanding rights and being seen as one of the more 'helpless' groups of people with disabilities awaiting assistance. At present they remain unnoticed between these two groups and are in danger of missing out because of it.

At the moment people with an acquired hearing loss are not seen as an identified group and in the main they do not identify themselves. They are not going to identify themselves as 'disabled' as long as current attitudes to disability exist. There is no real incentive to do so in a society where disability is perceived as an inequality alongside economic, sexual, and ethnic inequalities. It is more 'disabling' to admit to belonging to this category than to stay 'passing as normal'. Attitudes need to change so that people with a disability are seen as having a right to expect others to change to accommodate their needs, both on the public and private level. Only then will the needs of people with an acquired hearing loss become more visible.

The Research Project

CHOOSING THE POPULATION

The major problem with previous published studies, as we described in Chapter 2, was the lack of adequate control of socio-economic, personal, and age variables. We were anxious to avoid overrepresentation of professional groups and a weighting towards elderly people where adjustment might be confounded by other features. Details from four sources were used to create a precise quota sample according to job and geographical location. These sources were: previous project records held in the university; audiology clinic records; direct contact with outpatients at the ENT clinic; and an ongoing cardio-vascular study in the Bristol area.

People were matched by occupation to the census data for the areas of Avon in which they lived. They could then be divided into categories of recency of onset as shown in Table 5.1. The data for the pre-diagnostic sample is treated separately since they were all men and therefore did not match census statistics in the same way.

INTERVIEW FRAMEWORK

There were two interview stages: an initial one and a return visit ten months later. Following the pilot work, the interview format for the first stage was modified to include:

(i) initial brief questionnaire to determine suitability for inclusion in study;
(ii) extended questionnaire for hearing-impaired person – administered at home;
(iii) extended questionnaire for hearing person – administered at home and parallel to that of the hearing-impaired person;
(iv) communication exercise – the hearing person read a brief article to the hearing-impaired person;
(v) spectogram or family sculpture technique – this involved the use and placement of blocks by individuals to indicate how they individually or

jointly perceived the family relations (the technique is more fully described in Appendix 1);

(vi) both sections (iv) and (v) were audio recorded together with semi-structured discussion of hearing problems. These provided extended transcripts of the personal and 'family' views of hearing loss.

COMPLETING THE SCHEDULE

In order to meet the requirements for the sample and the interview, a series of stages were completed:

Stage 1: personal contact

The two interviewers (one hearing-impaired and one hearing) talked to people attending audiology and ENT clinics, or waiting for fittings or batteries for hearing aids. An initial short interview took place in a side room of a clinic, during which time permission was obtained to visit them at home for a further interview. This group contributed forty to our sample.

Stage 2: postal contact

For all those who had been interviewed in previous studies and those for whom records were available in the audiology clinic, a postal invitation was sent. Each letter was followed up by a telephone call and then a domiciliary visit. These groups contributed fifty-four to the sample.

Stage 3: pre-diagnostic sample

As the interviews progressed it became clear that adjustment to hearing loss had begun long before referral to the hearing services. For many people, their awareness of their hearing problem arose many years before they were fitted with a hearing aid. We therefore set out to examine a sample from the 'normal' population, i.e. those who could be contacted by routes other than the audiological services.

We obtained access to an ongoing cardio-vascular study of middle-aged men which had been run for five years by the Medical Research Council and the local district health authority. It had had a 92 per cent response rate in contacting men between 40 and 60 years of age via sixteen general practitioners. One of the questions they were asked was 'Do you have any difficulty hearing?' They were also given a brief screening for hearing loss at 50dB. We wrote to those answering 'Yes' to this question and failing the screening and followed them up by telephone, asking to see them. This produced a further twenty-nine participants. This group of hearing-impaired people, whom we took from the general population, were all male. The mean age overall was 48.4 years. The major difficulty with this group concerns the type of hearing loss they had. We have no data on nature and extent of hearing loss with this group other than the self-ratings. The possibility of a higher proportion of conductive losses in this group is a possibility which we cannot rule out at this time. The final numbers of those interviewed on the first occasion were therefore as in Table A1.

Table A1   Interviews completed (n=123)

	Hearing-impaired	Hearing	
Stage 1 contact	40	45	
Stage 2 contact	54	61	
Stage 3 contact	29	23	
Total	123	129	252

Table A.2 shows an occupational breakdown of the hearing-impaired families interviewed. The classification is according to the job of the head of household, whether or not this was the hearing-impaired person. This proved to be the most realistic socio-economic marker. Table A.3 shows the geographical distribution of interviewees.

SECOND PHASE INTERVIEWS

A sub-sample of the population was interviewed a second time. Details of job and recency of interview are shown in Table A.4.

On this occasion we were concerned about changes in attitude and adjustment to hearing loss. Expecting this to be greatest in those most recently diagnosed we concentrated on interviewing those with recency less than three years. As would be expected, the match to census figures in each category becomes less as the numbers decrease. Anomalies arise in the employer/manager category (too few) and in the unskilled manual (too many). Nevertheless, since these people are being compared with their own responses previously, they contribute important data on change over time.

Second interviews took place on average, 10.6 months after the first interview and on average 15.8 months after claimed issue of hearing aid.

The questionnaire data from the interviews lends itself to computer analysis

Table A2 shows an occupational breakdown of the hearing-impaired

Job of head of household	Recency of hearing-aid provision								Avon Census	
	(Pre-diagnosis)		(0–1 yr)		(2–5 yrs)		(6 yrs +)		Diagnosed total	No required	%
		Census		Census		Census		Census			
Professional	2	1.81	2	1.75	4	1.88	3	2.25	9	5.88	(6.25)
Employer/ manager	4	4.15	–	4.01	2	4.29	5	5.15	7	13.45	(14.31)
Junior/ non-manual	5	6.11	6	5.90	6	6.32	8	7.59	20	19.81	(21.07)
Skilled manual	11	8.54	7	8.24	7	8.83	9	10.59	23	27.66	(29.43)
Semi-skilled manual	4	4.02	3	3.88	5	4.16	5	5.00	13	13.04	(13.87)
Unskilled manual	–	1.28	3	1.24	3	1.33	2	1.59	8	4.16	(4.43)
Unemployed	2	2.38	1	2.29	–	2.45	2	2.96	3	7.70	(8.19)
Retired	1	0.36	3	0.35	2	0.38	2	0.45	7	1.18	(1.25)
Widowed	–	0.21	2	0.21	1	0.22	–	0.25	3	0.68	(0.73)
Student	–	0.14	1	0.13	–	0.14	–	0.17	1	0.44	(0.47)
	29	(29)	28	(28)	30	(30)	36	(36)	94	(n=94)	(100)

Table A3 Interviews completed arranged by district (hearing aids issued n=94)

Job of head of household	Bristol (n=54)	Avon Census	Kings-wood (n=7)	Avon Census	North Avon (n=18)	Avon Census	Wans-dyke (n=6)	Avon Census	Wood-spring (n=9)	Avon Census	Interview total (n=94)	Avon Census	Avon Census (%)
Professional	2	2.74	2	0.42	1	1.62	1	0.42	3	0.66	9	5.88	(6.25)
Employer/manager	4	5.83	1	1.10	1	3.23	1	1.27	–	1.92	7	13.45	(14.31)
Junior/non-manual	10	11.51	–	1.47	10	3.68	–	1.11	–	2.05	20	19.81	(21.07)
Skilled manual	11	15.74	3	2.38	4	5.44	2	1.82	3	2.29	23	27.66	(29.43)
Semi-skilled manual	9	8.11	–	0.90	2	2.36	1	0.72	1	0.97	13	13.04	(13.87)
Unskilled manual	7	3.07	–	0.22	–	0.46	1	0.19	–	0.26	8	4.16	(4.43)
Unemployed	3	5.55	–	0.38	–	0.90	–	0.32	–	0.61	3	7.70	(8.19)
Retired	4	0.72	1	0.07	–	0.17	–	0.09	2	0.14	7	1.18	(1.25)
Widowed	3	0.49	–	0.03	–	0.06	–	0.03	–	0.06	3	0.68	(0.73)
Student	1	0.24	–	0.03	–	0.08	–	0.03	–	0.04	1	0.44	(0.47)
			7		18		6		9		94		(100)

Table A4 Second interviews

Job of head of household	Category 1 (pre-diagnosis)	Census	Category 2 (0–1 yr)	Census	Category 3 (2–3 yrs)	Census	Interview total	Avon Census No	%
Professional	0	0.06	1	1.25	2	0.81	3	2.12	(6.25)
Employer/ manager	0	0.14	0	2.86	1	1.86	1	4.86	(14.31)
Junior/ non-manual	1	0.21	5	4.21	1	2.74	7	7.16	(21.07)
Skilled manual	0	0.30	7	5.89	5	3.83	12	10.01	(29.43)
Semi-skilled manual	0	0.14	1	2.77	0	1.80	1	4.72	(13.87)
Unskilled manual	0	0.04	2	0.89	2	0.58	4	1.51	(4.43)
Unemployed	0	0.08	1	1.64	0	1.07	1	2.78	(8.19)
Retired	0	0.01	1	0.25	1	0.16	2	0.43	(1.25)
Widowed	0	0.01	2	0.15	1	0.09	3	0.25	(0.73)
Student	0	0.01	0	0.09	0	0.06	0	0.16	(0.47)
	1	(n=1)	20	(n=20)	13	(n=13)	34	(n=34)	(100)

The questionnaire data from the interviews lends itself to computer analysis and this has been the principal means of approach. However, this data has then been validated with the personal interviews which have been recorded and transcribed. (details in Appendix 2). It is clear that the questionnaires appear to have been a constraining feature in data collection perhaps leading to a narrowing of response. At the same time, the task of analysing transcripts has proved extremely complex but has yielded a rich source of data. The two sets of analyses, nevertheless, in complementing one another, provide a key insight into the workings and development of relationships when hearing loss occurs.

Characteristics of the interviews

The in-depth interviews took place with 123 hard-of-hearing people and their families, mainly at home. Four people elected to come in and be interviewed at the university. The method chosen was a semi-structured interview with a check-list of topics to be summarized at the end. The topics raised were selected from a series of six pilot interviews which were held with people contacted via the local tinnitus group.

The issues which emerged from these preliminary sessions as appearing most commonly were given as groups of characteristics around which to group the data collected. The following topics were seen as central.

PERCEPTIONS OF, AND BELIEFS ABOUT, DEAFNESS FOR BOTH HEARING AND HARD-OF-HEARING PEOPLE

These included:
1 Hope for a cure
2 Knowing other people with hearing loss
3 Association with ageing
4 Changed job prospects
5 Notions of 'perseverance', and seeking help
6 Beliefs about disability
7 Fear of the future
8 What it feels like to experience hearing loss from both sides

SOCIAL CONTEXT OF HEARING LOSS – FOR BOTH PARTNERS

1 Disclosing to strangers
2 Other people's responses
3 Children

4 Embarrassment
5 'Passing' in a hearing world

THE 'PROCESS' OF HEARING LOSS – FOR BOTH PARTNERS

1   How it happened
2   Seeking help
3   Diagnosis
4   The helping professions
5   Other illnesses
6   Other effects
7   Reaction
8   Depression
9   Adapting
10 Avoidance
11 Acceptance
12 Private hearing aids/private health care

THE 'MECHANICS' OF DAILY LIFE – FOR BOTH PARTNERS

1 Noise in the home
2 Hearing-aid use
3 Strategies and tactics
4 Tinnitus
5 Meeting new people
6 Environmental aids

RELATIONSHIPS

1   Control
2   Intimate talk
3   Parenting
4   Dependency
5   Joking and laughter
6   Significant others
7   Irritability
8   Conflict
9   Blame
10 Noise within the home and dealing with it
11 The future
12 Dealing with the outside world

Now, obviously, some of these are overlapping categories – for instance, disclosing a hearing loss to strangers is part of the 'mechanics' of everyday life, as well as how two people or a family cope with their feelings about dealing with the outside world.

These groupings, though, were used as the basis of indexing the data on the first analysis. The next stage was to develop relationships between these categories. The concepts and categories obviously developed as the work progressed through the analysis of earlier interviews.

Each interview was tape-recorded and transcribed. Both interviewers made notes as to the general 'feel' of the interview. The semi-structured talk came at the end of a questionnaire, so to a certain extent people expected our questions to be about 'communication' and hearing aids as the questions had been. We felt it was important, though, to build in an element of qualitative research – looking at 'what things exist, rather than to determine how many such things there are' (Hedges 1981). The reason for this was that hearing loss and its effects on relationships emerged as a complex and sensitive subject which requires an understanding of that complexity beyond that which is achieved in an interview schedule. We wanted a consumer's view of the situation from the people directly involved with the issue and who had a wide range of knowledge and experience to bring to bear on the subject. In order to get at this knowledge and experience the respondents were encouraged to relate in their own terms the sense they made of their own 'world', their own experience. The respondent's own taxonomy – for instance, the word 'deaf', or 'trouble with my hearing', or 'my ear problem' – was the one used throughout the interview.

The following is a summary of the 'households' interviewed. Numbers in brackets indicate the number of people interviewed.

DIAGNOSED GROUP

Interview 1 (2) Young married couple, early 30s, two young children. The husband had lost some hearing aged 24 years in a bomb blast whilst in the army and lost his hearing completely at 33 years. Became unemployed two months before this happened and still was unemployed two years later at time of interview. The only couple to use sign language (supporting speech) during interview. Contacted via sign-language class. No longer able to wear an aid.

Interview 2 (2) Married couple in their 50s – recent second marriage for both. Both said they had a mild hearing loss and tinnitus, contacted via the tinnitus group. Neither wore a hearing aid.

Interview 3 (2) Married couple, early 50s, wife had developed a hearing loss after repeated ear infections at 41 years old. Secretary of local tinnitus group, had worn a hearing aid for eight years. Contacted via local tinnitus group.

Interview 4 (2,2) Married couple in late 40s. Wife had recently (two weeks before first interview) had hearing aid after being told at work to go and get one (she worked as a shop-assistant.) At second interview hadn't worn her aid for six months. Both seemed to want to deny it was happening. Contacted via audiology clinic. Interviewed twice.

Interview 5 (2,1) Single parent, woman of 41 born in Jamaica originally, an auxiliary nurse in a mental handicap hospital. Three daughters in their late teens, one away from home at college, one training as a nurse, and one doing A levels. Had had trouble with her hearing for at least six years, had just got aid at first home interview, at second home interview much improved and more outgoing. Contacted via audiology clinic. Interviewed twice.

Interview 6 (3) Married couple late 40s, three daughters, 16, 20, 24. Wife had had hearing loss for ten years. Hearing aid for three years but 'never wears it' (wore it at interview). Contacted via audiology clinic.

Interview 7 (2) Married couple, wife 59, husband 60, retired from working in Africa, wife had previously been a nursing sister. She had had a hearing aid (but hardly ever wore it) for only a couple of weeks after a sudden but mild loss sometime before. Husband also complained of hearing loss, waiting to go for fitting for hearing aid. Contacted via audiology clinic. Two sons, grown up, away from home.

Interview 8 (2,2) Married couple, wife 59, husband 60, retired. Wife had a long-time hearing loss, but only had aid two weeks before first home interview. One year later, first big improvement after wearing aid, much more outgoing. Interviewed twice.

Interview 9 (3) 20-year-old, male student, shared flat with two others, one his girl-friend. A mild fluctuating hearing loss over one year. Hereditary hearing loss in family, father and one brother hard-of-hearing. Very bad tinnitus 'ever since I can remember'. Tested for aid but told not bad enough, he felt they'd got him 'on a good day'. Difficulty hearing lectures, worked in disco part-time, which caused increased tinnitus and hearing loss for couple of days afterwards.

Interview 10 (2) Married couple in their 50s, both civil servants, no children. Elderly father living with them. Husband had otosclerosis for six years, hearing aid for six months, which he 'hardly ever' wore. Difficulty at work hearing conversations.

Interview 11 (2,1) Married couple in their early 30s, two children 5 and 3. Husband art dealer, own gallery, had moderate hearing loss for three and a half years, obtained aid after first interview, not noticeably helped by it one year later. Finding work difficult because of it. Private consultation initially (related to consultant). Contacted via audiology clinic. Interviewed twice.

Interview 12 (2) Married couple in their early 30s, three children, 8, 6, and 9 months. Wife had had hearing aid for four years, a hearing loss for six years since birth of her second child. Contacted via audiology clinic.

Interview 13 (2) Married couple in their 40s. Wife had operation which had improved her hearing, as had wearing an aid for past four years. Second marriage (nine years previously) so husband had only known her since she had a hearing loss. She had worked as a cook. Three grown-up children. Contacted via audiology clinic.

Interview 14 (2,2) Married couple in their early 30s. One son aged 8 who also had a hearing loss. Husband, a newsagent, had a perforated ear drum seven and a half years previously and had worn a hearing aid for 18 months. Found dealing with customers a problem but managed. Contacted via audiology clinic. Interviewed twice.

Interview 15 (2,2) Married couple in their early 40s, two children aged 9 and 14. Husband had had a mastoid as a child but no hearing problem until last three years. Hearing aid fitted just before first interview – doesn't wear aid. Lost job because of hearing loss. Contacted via audiology clinic. Interviewed twice.

Interview 16 (2) Married couple in their 50s. Wife had had a hearing loss for ten years. Eight years with an aid. Adopted son of 15 years. Husband 'didn't want to know'. Contacted via audiology clinic.

Interview 17 (2,2) Married couple in 40s. (Second marriage for husband.) Two children of the marriage, aged 16 and 12. Husband, a lorry mechanic, had sudden severe dramatic hearing loss after a serious heart attack. Improvement in hearing by second interview, but constant fear of relapse. Had hearing aid on day of first home interview. Contacted via audiology clinic. Interviewed twice.

Interview 18 (1) Man aged 34, lived alone. Traumatic loss three months after a car accident, ruptured ear drum. GP neglected it, two days sickness and pain. Five years before interview, lost job as theatre designer. Trying to restart freelance as props maker. Suffered from severe tinnitus. Contacted via audiology clinic.

Interview 19 (2,2) Married couple in 50s. Grown-up children. Husband, an engineering estimator, had had hearing aid for two months at first home interview. Suffered from tinnitus very badly – 'every day a struggle'. At second interview said he wasn't wearing aid. Interviewed twice.

Interview 20 (1) 27-year-old man, lived alone. Traumatic severe hearing loss following a car accident when he was 19-years-old. He had to give up his job as a nurse in a mental handicap hospital, his fiancée broke off engagement. He was unemployed at the time of the interview but was working as a volunteer on a hearing-aid follow-up scheme. He wore two hearing aids and was learning a little sign language. Suffered from tinnitus. Contacted via audiology clinic.

Interview 21 (1,1) Married woman, 54, husband not there at either of interviews – a fireman, called out twice. Two daughters 19 and 27. Mild hearing loss for three years. Had got hearing aid one month before first home interview. By second interview wasn't wearing it, even at work (as shop-assistant). Suffered from tinnitus. Contacted via audiology clinic. Interviewed twice.

Interview 22 (1) 54-year-old married man (wife not present at interview). Hospital porter, had had a mild hearing loss for thirteen years, Meniere's disease, but had only got a hearing aid one month before interview. Suffered from tinnitus and from 'nerves' he said. Contacted via audiology clinic.

Interview 23 (2,1) Housewife aged 48 years, married, but interviewed with 18-year-old daughter. Had one son, 10 years old and one daughter. Twenty years of 'trouble with her hearing'. Had previously worked as childminder. Waiting for hearing aid to be fitted at first home interview, had previously visited a private consultant nine years before. Had waited a long time before going to seek help but felt 'forced into it by her family'. She also had tinnitus. Contacted via audiology clinic. Interviewed twice.

Interview 24 (3,1) Married couple in their 50s. Four grown-up children, two still at home. Husband a hospital porter, mild hearing loss for eight years. First hearing aid fitted one month before first home interview. Doesn't wear aid much because he is embarrassed by it. Contacted via audiology clinic. Interviewed twice.

Interview 25 (2) Married couple in their 40s. Children aged 10 and 12 years. Husband a commercial traveller, had had a hearing loss for four years and a hearing aid for eighteen months. He had had two operations, one which caused a gradual decline, then one which showed a marked improvement. By second home interview, however, this improvement had disappeared. He also suffered with tinnitus. Interviewed twice.

Interview 26 (3,2) A widow aged 53 with a 16-year-old daughter and 22-year-old son at home. Two other children lived nearby. At first home interview, the son and a married daughter were there. The respondent had had an operation for a perforated eardrum six months before the interview after ear infections for 'years'. She was waiting for a hearing aid at first interview. She also had epilepsy and diabetes. Interviewed twice.

Interview 27 (2) Married couple in their early 30s. Two sons aged 2 years and 1 year. The wife had otosclerosis for thirteen years and a hearing aid for ten years. A second marriage for her, so they had only known each other since she'd been hard-of-hearing. She'd given up theatre nursing because of the hearing loss and now worked two nights a week in a geriatric hospital (with difficulty). Her husband was a nurse in a mental handicap hospital. The two babies caused problems with waking up at night. The respondent also had tinnitus. Contacted via audiology clinic.

Interview 28 (3) A 45-year-old woman, a single parent (recently divorced) with three teenage children. Worked as a shop-assistant. Respondent had had a hearing loss for twelve years, after otitis media fifteen years before. Also had tinnitus. Managed very well. Two daughters present at interview. Contacted via audiology clinic.

Interview 29 (2) A married couple in their 50s. Wife worked as a shop-assistant. She had had a hearing aid for ten years and hearing problems for thirty years. Had an operation at 28 years of age (now 57). Suffered from tinnitus. Contacted via audiology clinic.

Interview 30 (2,1) Young married couple in early 30s. Wife had hearing problems for eight years, hearing aid for three years. Worse with the birth of two daughters (at time of interview 6 and 8 years old). Husband a driving instructor, wife at home but working in a factory at second interview, part-time. Finding hearing problems difficult, also had tinnitus. Interviewed twice.

Interview 31 (2) Married couple in their 40s, grown-up son lived away. Husband and wife interviewed. Husband had 'messy ear infections' for years, went to hospital one year before and had had operation two months before visit – much improved. Respondent also had heart disease – a 'more worrying' problem. He had tinnitus. Contacted through audiology clinic.

Interview 32 (3) Married couple in their 40s. Wife with a severe hearing loss since she was 21, using a hearing aid for twenty years. She worked as a cleaner/driver for a baker, and her husband was a dustman. Two sons aged 15 and 19 years. The respondent also had tinnitus. Contacted via audiology clinic.

Interview 33 (2,2) Woman of 30 years, lived with her mother, present at both interviews. Respondent worked in a tobacco factory, noisy environment, had hearing problems for four years and was waiting for a hearing aid at first home interview. Also suffered from tinnitus. Contacted via audiology clinic. Interviewed twice.

Interview 34 (2) Married couple in their 40s, husband a lorry driver, six children – 3 foster sons, only the eldest, 25 years, not at home. Offered hearing aid just before first home interview but refused it, felt he could manage without. Asked people to sit on the right side of him, doesn't feel it's a problem – wife thinks 'if he isn't worried, I'm not'.

Interview 35 (2,1) Schoolteacher of 53, divorced with one son still living at home (23 years) and one away. She lived with her elderly father as well.

239

She had tinnitus and had been having trouble with her hearing for nine years, was waiting for an aid at the first home interview. At second interview wasn't wearing aid at all, despite struggles at school to keep up with what was going on. Grandparents and mother all hard-of-hearing. Contacted via audiology clinic. Interviewed twice.

Interview 36 (1) Married woman aged 48, interviewed alone ('led separate life from husband', she said). Worked part-time as secretary. Mild hearing loss for many years. Tinnitus for five years. Had just received aid at home interview, which she felt was a help at work. Was worried about finding new job because of her hearing, as her boss was retiring.

Interview 37 (2) Married couple in their late 30s, son aged 18 years, daughter aged 16 years. Husband had a hearing loss for 'years', gradually getting worse, especially in last ten years. Hearing aid for nine years and worked as a company director. Teenage children a problem.

Interview 38 (3,2) Married couple in their 50s, six children – all away from home except the youngest – 22 years. Wife previously a machinist in noisy factory, had hearing loss for one year, hearing aid for one month at first home interview. At second interview was 'hardly ever' wearing it. Suffered from tinnitus. Interviewed twice.

Interview 39 (2) Married couple in their 50s. Husband had a dramatic unexpected loss after an ear operation 'for wax in his ears', after years of infections. He now had hearing loss and bad tinnitus and had been using a hearing aid for one year.

Interview 40 (3) Married couple in their 50s, with 22-year-old son, present at interview. Wife a post-office clerk, developed otitis media twelve years previously. Had operation privately which resulted in a sudden decrease in hearing and increased tinnitus. Hearing aid worn ever since. Hoping for a cure. Contacted via records and previous project.

Interview 41 (2) Married couple in their early 50s, husband a salesman. Sudden loss after an ear operation for ear infection. Hearing aid for six years. Two children – 28 and 25 years, lived away from home. Cheerful personality, fed up with being treated as 'daft'. Also had tinnitus. Contacted via hospital records and from previous project.

Interview 42 (2) Married couple in their late 40s. Two daughters, one still at home – 19 years. Husband a television repairer, had a stapedectomy at 29 years with a marked improvement in his hearing which had since declined. He had had a hearing aid for one year. In a way, two experiences of hearing loss, but was finding the second situation harder to cope with. Contacted via hospital records and previous project.

Interview 43 (3) Married couple in their late 40s. Two sons, one aged 15 still at home. The husband had had a hearing aid for three years and a hearing loss for six years, as well as tinnitus.

Interview 44 (2) Married couple in their 30s, two children 14 and 11 years. The wife had had a hearing aid for eight years (although her husband said fifteen years). Both hoped for a 'cure' and were seeking 'private' help for an operation having been told she had an 'inoperable' hearing problem by the NHS. She never wore her hearing aid so relied on facing people to follow conversation. Contacted via records.

Interview 45 (2) Married couple in their 50s, living with their 26-year-old daughter and the wife's sister who had Down's Syndrome. The husband, an ambulance driver, had had a hearing aid for five years, which he only took out to play the double bass at the evangelical church to which they both belonged. Was having faith healing for his hearing which he said was working well.

Interview 46 (4) Married couple in their late 40s, lived with their two daughters – 12 and 16 years, and the elderly parents of the wife. The husband had 'trouble' in one ear for years since they were courting, twenty-four years before, but awoke one morning with a sudden dramatic loss in the other ear, four years before interview. He'd had a hearing aid for two years before the home interview. Contacted via records and previous project.

Interview 47 (2) Married couple, no children, husband late 40s, wife early 30s. Husband had had a car accident two years previously, leaving him with a mild hearing loss but with none of the spinal injury and paralysis that they first feared. He was an RSPCA inspector and she was a veterinary student. He had had a hearing aid for three months, he also suffered from tinnitus. Contacted via audiology clinic.

Interview 48 (2,2) Female teacher of 48, living with a friend the same age. The respondent had had a hearing aid for five years and was waiting for a second aid to be fitted for the other ear. She'd suffered with otosclerosis and had had a stapedectomy seventeen years previously. She also had tinnitus. By the second interview the hard-of-hearing respondent had been on sick leave for a year and was giving up teaching because of her hearing loss. Contacted via records. Interviewed twice.

Interview 49 (2) Married couple in their 50s. One son who lived away. The husband, a labourer, had had twenty years of a mild hearing loss and was waiting for a hearing aid at first home interview. By the second interview was 'transformed' by it, taking much more part in things, and regretted not having got one years before. He also had tinnitus. Contacted via records. Interviewed twice.

Interview 50 (2) Married couple in their 50s with two grown-up sons living away. The husband, whilst a teacher, had bilateral acoustic neuroma thirteen years before – profound hearing loss seven years later. Very severe tinnitus. He had left teaching because of the hearing loss and became a gardener. His wife who was born in Cyprus worked in a tobacco factory. Contacted via records and previous project.

Interview 51 (3) Married couple in late 40s, husband a shipyard welder (noisy workplace). One son 21, away from home. One daughter 17. The husband had had a hearing aid for ten years and two operations, one successful, one not. He had a moderate hearing loss and tinnitus. Contacted via records.

Interview 52 (3,2) Married couple in their 50s, living with 25-year-old son and 90-year-old mother of husband. The husband, a printer in a noisy workplace, had had a hearing aid for five years, but never wears it 'except to go to the doctor's'. Contacted via hospital records. Interviewed twice.

Interview 53 (2) Married couple in the 40s, three sons, 21, 17, and 12 years. The wife had a moderate/severe hearing loss for eight years since a perforated eardrum after swimming. She'd had a hearing aid for seven years and constant ear infections and tinnitus. Previously had a mastoid as a child. The husband was an antique dealer, the wife at home. Contacted via hospital records.

Interview 54 (2) Married couple in 50s, husband recently retired early, wife at home. The husband had had a moderate hearing loss for five years and a hearing aid for two years, only worn for watching TV. Daughter, absent at interview, aged 28, lived at home. Contacted via records and earlier project.

Interview 55 (2) Married couple in late 30s, two children aged 10 and 5 years. Wife had previously been a telephonist but had given up because of hearing loss. She had had a hearing aid for eight years, and had started to suffer from moderate/severe 'nerve deafness' after the birth of their first child. Her mother was also hard-of-hearing.

Interview 56 (2) Married couple in their 50s, husband a senior lecturer, wife a GP. The husband had had a moderate hearing loss, 'nerve deafness', for six years although his wife said he'd been slightly hard-of-hearing since a student, thirty years before. He'd had a hearing aid for three years (which he never wore). He also had tinnitus.

Interview 57 (2) Married couple, in their late 20s. Two daughters aged 2 years and 3 months. The husband, a civil servant, had had a hearing aid for three years, but didn't wear it. Contacted via records.

Interview 58 (2,1) Married couple in their 40s. Four children from 4 to 12 years old. The husband, an antiquarian bookseller, had had a hearing aid for two years but rarely wore it except for meetings. He also has tinnitus and had had otosclerosis for four or five years. Contacted via records and previous project. Interviewed twice.

Interview 59 (1,1) A widow in her late 50s, living alone, who'd had a moderate hearing loss for five years and a hearing aid for six months at first home interview. A rather frail woman who also had tinnitus and cataracts and who was looking after her 18-month-old grandchild full-time and staying at daughter's during the week. By second interview was wearing aid and had had cataract operation. Felt 'a new person'. Contacted via records. Interviewed twice.

Interview 60 (3) Married couple in their 50s. The husband, an engineer, had had a hearing aid for six years after fourteen years of 'problems' with a moderate hearing loss (otosclerosis). Three sons, aged 18–22 years (eldest away from home). Contacted via records.

Interview 61 (2) Married couple in their 40s. Husband an engineer, went to doctor's with 'blocked' ears after a cold, eight years ago, having not heard properly for 'quite a while'. Hearing aid for five years. Also has tinnitus. There is a grown-up daughter who lives away from home. Contacted via records and earlier project.

Interview 62 (2) Married couple, husband 42, wife 38. The husband, who was also visually handicapped (registered blind) but with some sight, had had a hearing aid for four years but hadn't worn it since successful operation. He'd had two operations for otosclerosis, the second of which had improved his hearing. His father was hearing-impaired and his mother was visually handicapped, both his sensory impairments were hereditary. Husband worked as a caretaker. Contacted via records.

Interview 63 (2) Married couple in their 40s, four sons 17–12 years, one who has spina bifida was away at residential school during the week. The husband had otosclerosis, and had been given an aid seven years before which he stopped wearing after one year. He also had tinnitus. A very musical family who all sang in a choir. Contacted via records and previous project.

Interview 64 (2,2) Married couple in early 30s (only married one week at first home interview). Two sons aged 11 and 9 years from wife's first marriage (widowed). The wife had a profound hearing loss which had begun gradually at 22, after the birth of her first child, finally lost her hearing completely two years before interview. Previously had worn two hearing aids. Had been a single parent for nine years after her husband's death, from a brain tumour, when she was 23 years old, with a 6-month-old baby and a 2-year-old child. Her second husband was a printer, she was a 'home economics executive' as she called being a housewife. She also had tinnitus and was waiting to have a cochlear implant. Contacted via records and previous project. Communicated by writing and lip-reading. Disliked sign language. Interviewed twice.

Interview 65 (3) Married couple, wife in late 20s, husband 41, with two daughters, aged 6 and 3. Wife had had a hearing aid for three years (mother also had one) after problems for 'years'. Also had tinnitus. Contacted via records.

Interview 66 (2) Married couple in their 40s, husband a storeman. Hearing aid for six years – moderate/severe loss, after ten years of problems (his account), twenty-four years (his wife's account). Daughter 23, at home, son 21, away. Contacted via records.

Interview 67 (2) Married couple in their early 30s, no children. Husband, a labourer, had been invalided out of the army with a severe hearing loss after repeated ear infections. Had box hearing aid privately, fourteen years before, then had got NHS aids in 1982 (one in each ear). He also had tinnitus. Contacted via records and previous project.

Interview 68 (1) Single mother, three boys aged 14 and 9 years. Part-time speech therapist. Hearing aid for six days at first home interview, after eight years of a moderate hearing loss. Her father had become hard-of-hearing. Contacted via audiology clinic.

Interview 69 (3) Married couple in their 40s, husband a manager at aerospace factory, had otosclerosis and two operations fifteen years earlier. Had worn an aid for fifteen years, the first one bought privately. Felt the aid had transformed his life and that of his family. Two daughters aged 19 and 21 years. The elder one lived away. Contacted via records and earlier project.

Interview 70 (3) Married couple in their 40s, four children, only two at home – 19 and 15 years. Husband, a social worker, had had a hearing aid for eight years, and two aids for each ear for a year. Severe hearing loss. Father and sister hard-of-hearing. He also had tinnitus. Contacted via records and previous project.

Interview 71 (3) Married couple in their 40s. One daughter 18, one son 20, at home. Husband had had hearing aid for two years and a hearing loss for twenty-two years. Very keen on music. Contacted via records and previous project.

Interview 72 (2) Deputy headmistress in her 40s, married but husband away at interview. 23-year-old daughter at home, 20-year-old son away. The respondent had had a hearing aid for three years after a fluctuating hearing loss of four years' duration following ear infection. At the time of the interview her hearing was 'very good' she felt, and much improved. She also had tinnitus. Interested in alternative medicine. Contacted via records.

Interview 73 (2) Married couple in their 50s. Daughter 31 years old at home, son 36 years old lived away. Husband a marketing manager had had a hearing aid for eight years, but rarely wore it (still had the same set of batteries he was given eight years ago!) He had had otosclerosis and a moderate hearing loss for twelve years, his mother had been hard-of-hearing. The respondent also had tinnitus. Contacted via records and previous project.

Interview 74 (2) Married couple in their 50s. One son lived in a separate flat in their house. The wife had had a hearing aid for eighteen years, moderate/severe loss. A private aid after a large box NHS one meant she felt much better and wore her post-aural aid all the time. The husband worked for the Gas Board, the wife was retired from working in school canteen after a mastectomy operation. Contacted via records.

Interview 75 (3) Married couple (husband 55 years old, wife 38 years old). The wife had had a hearing aid for five years but 'hardly ever' wore it. Moderate loss for eight to ten years. Daughters 21, 19, 16 years. Eldest away from home. The respondent worked as a home help with the elderly and her husband worked as a quality control inspector

Interview 76 (2) Married couple in their 40s. Three grown-up children (in their 20s) living at home. Husband, a chauffeur, wife a part-time shop-assistant. The wife had otosclerosis and had worn an aid for eleven years – 'a life-line' for a moderate/severe hearing loss. Hearing loss in both families. Contacted via records and previous project.

Interview 77 (2) Married couple in their 40s with two grown-up sons (one at home with broken neck in plaster after rugby accident). Wife not present at interview. Husband an electrical engineer, wife a nurse. The husband had worn hearing aid for ten years and relied on it. Contacted via records and previous project.

Interview 78 (2) Married couple in their 30s (married six months). Husband a chartered surveyor had had a hearing loss for ten years after a hereditary mild/moderate hearing loss. Didn't wear aid very often, found it an embarrassment. Contacted via records.

Interview 79 (1) A driving instructor in his 40s, a single parent with four children (teenagers still at home). He'd worn a hearing aid for six years after a sudden dramatic hearing loss after an operation.

Interview 80 (3) Married couple in their early 50s, four grown-up children, only one boy, 19 years, at home. The wife, a nursing auxiliary, had had otosclerosis for at least ten years, with a sudden dramatic decline after an operation. Had been issued with a hearing aid eight years before but rarely wore it. Moderate hearing loss. Husband a British Telecom engineer. Contacted via records and previous project.

Interview 81 (1) Married couple in their 40s. Three grown-up children, two still at home. Husband had sudden severe hearing loss after eighteen years in Army – left and found another job. Had a heart attack two days after starting new job – changed jobs again. Hearing aid for ten years, which he 'relied upon'. He also suffered from severe tinnitus. Contacted via records.

Interview 82 (1) Man in his 20s, lived alone. Graduate computer pro-grammer. Mild loss – he'd had a hearing aid for two years but never wore it: 'too much trouble'. Also had occasional tinnitus. Contacted via records and previous project.

Interview 83 (2) Married couple, wife late 50s, husband retired in 60s. Wife had had a hearing loss for six years after otosclerosis diagnosed. She never wore the aid, she 'liked living in her quiet peaceful world', she said. Husband also had a mild hearing loss. Contacted via records.

Interview 84 (2) Married couple in early 50s, one foster child aged 11 years. Husband first had operation for otosclerosis twenty years before, then two more operations, the last one unsuccessful. He had had hearing aid for six years. His wife said he never wore it at home. Contacted via records and previous project.

Interview 85 (2) Married couple in their 30s, two sons aged 9 and 5 years. Wife had otosclerosis, moderate loss, before meeting husband. Loss deteriorated after birth of first child. She had worn aid for seven years. Both husband and wife were schoolteachers. The wife also had tinnitus. Contacted via records and previous project.

Interview 86 (2) Married couple in their late 40s. Two daughters away from home. Wife had otosclerosis. A problem for several years before going to hospital. Hearing aid seven months before first home interview. Had given up job as shop-assistant. Husband an antique dealer. Contacted via records and previous project.

Interview 87 (2) Married couple in their early 20s. Wife had had hearing aid for two years. Gradual loss for seven years and tinnitus. Wife worked as kitchen assistant, husband as a labourer. Contacted via audiology clinic.

Interview 88 (2) Man of 33, a gardener living with his mother and 29-year-old sister who was mentally handicapped. He'd had a hearing aid for eleven years after a perforated eardrum although his mother said she'd been hit on the ear by a snowball when she was pregnant with him and he'd 'always been deaf'. Contacted via records.

Interview 89 (1) Married couple, three children aged 8–14 years. Wife had worn a hearing aid for eleven years which she relied upon after otosclerosis. She also suffered from tinnitus. Husband worked as a foreman, she was a housewife.

Interview 90 (2) Married couple. Husband in his 40s, a process worker. Had had a hearing aid for seven years but never wore it. Thought his loss was due to a car accident. He also had tinnitus. Daughter aged 17 years, son 19 years. Contacted via records.

Interview 91 (1) Married couple, husband alone at interview (wife called away by son's minor accident). 27-year-old electrician on a building site, had had a hearing aid for seven years but never wore it, had lent it to his mother. He'd had a fall at judo which had 'done something' to the nerves in his ears, he said. Mild/moderate loss, also had tinnitus. Contacted via records.

Interview 92 (1) Married couple in their 50s. Husband alone at interview, wife visiting daughter in hospital unexpectedly. He had suffered hearing loss five years previously when in hospital after heart attack (the first of five attacks). He'd had a hearing aid for four years but never wore it. Two grown-up children away from home, mother-in-law lived with them.

Interview 93 (2,2) Married couple in their early 30s. Three children 10, 6, and 2 years. Husband a fork-lift truck driver, had had aid for two years at first interview. Never wore it at home, and by second interview not at all. Difficulties in communicating. Interviewed twice.

Interview 94 (1) Freelance writer in 50s, interviewed alone. Married (for second time). Previously worked in radio until sudden severe hearing loss four years before. Two children 22 and 24 years, lived away from home. Suffered from tinnitus. Contacted via records and previous project.

PRE-DIAGNOSTIC GROUP

Interview 101 (1) Married couple, husband retired early, working temporarily as draughtsman, wife a nurse also retired early. Husband had never been to a doctor about his hearing but said he definitely had had problems for ten years which he thought were to do with working in a noisy environment as a sheet-metal worker for a number of years. He said he always 'had to concentrate' listening to speech and found himself 'making a guess' a lot of the time at what was being said. His wife described him as hearing-impaired. He seemed unconcerned by his hearing loss and enjoyed life, keeping bees and following his other interests.

Interview 102 (1) A widower with three daughters, one had left home recently, the youngest aged 20 years. An industrial engineer, the respondent had suffered from ear infections, hearing loss and tinnitus for the previous five yeas. He'd seen the ENT consultant four years before who had recommended an operation. Fearful of the operation he hadn't been back. He could no longer hear the phone ringing or follow conversation without effort, and was worried about his daughters leaving home because of the phone and doorbell. His daughters were 'no help' he said and kept saying 'don't bother'.

Interview 103 (2) Married couple with six children, three at home, one with a mental handicap. Husband in late 50s, foreman in a flour mill, had had trouble with hearing and tinnitus for five years. He'd been to the doctor once for the tinnitus but he'd been 'no help' so he saw 'no point in going back'. His 'mates' covered up for him at work, it was fine, he said, because he was foreman. At home he never heard the phone ring or answered it, everyone had to shout, his wife said, and TV noise was a problem. Noisy workplace for years. He felt unconcerned by his hearing loss, his wife however felt 'exasperated'.

Interview 104 (2) Married couple in their 50s, husband a storeman in a noisy workplace, had cattarrh which affected his hearing. He'd been to the doctor about a chest infection and had mentioned it, had had his ears syringed the previous year. Still wasn't hearing properly, his wife said it was worse than he did. He was worried about it declining, his mother had had a hearing loss.

Interview 105 (2) Married couple in the 50s, husband foreman in the shoe trade (noisy workplace). He'd had a hearing loss for three years and was waiting to go into hospital for an operation on a perforated eardrum, after having gone to the doctor because of the smell of the discharge rather than the hearing loss. Everyone at work shouted above the noise of the machinery anyway, so he managed at work, he said. At home his wife said she was used to it as her foster-mother had been deaf, but the noise of TV caused arguments.

Interview 106 (2) Married couple in their early 50s, no children. Very active and fit, cycling and keep-fit enthusiasts. He'd previously been a keen diver and swimmer and had had to give up because it hurt his ears and he'd got a discharge from his ears. In his job as a foreman in building maintenance, he said he had real problems giving instructions because he could no longer judge the tone of his voice, so he watched people's faces and often realized he'd got it wrong. He'd been to his GP who syringed his ears regularly but that 'didn't make much difference'. He had a fear of being 'cut up' if the GP sent him to the hospital, so didn't press the matter. 'If they start carving up your ears, you're in dead trouble'. TV noise was a problem at home and he and his wife argued a lot about that and then constant repetition. He said that socially 'when it's bad, it's pretty grim', referring to the effect his hearing had. Both acknowledged his 'deafness' and didn't seem put out by it unduly.

Interview 107 (2) Married couple in their 50s, grown-up children. Husband, a meat manager, had very slight trouble hearing, couldn't hear bird song for instance, otherwise no real problems.

Interview 108 (1) A motor mechanic in his 50s, living with his mother after separating from his wife and 16-year-old son. He worked in a noisy workplace, where he asked people to shout, couldn't use the phone properly, sat at the front at meetings and found he 'switched off' mentally in conversation. He had never consulted a doctor because he saw 'no reason to burden the doctor with my problems'. He continued going to the occupational health nurse to have his ears syringed regularly.

Interview 109 (2) Married couple in their 50s, no children. Husband a driver delivering meat, had had a hearing loss and tinnitus for thirty-five years since suffering a perforated eardrum in the RAF from the noise of guns. He'd never been to the hospital, but went to have his ears syringed at the

GP's every two years. He had considerable difficulty following conversation and a continuous discharge from one ear and a 'popping sensation' a couple of hours after waking, which sometimes helped him to hear better for a few hours. He felt it was just one of those things 'you have to live with'. His wife was more anxious, felt he should get a hearing aid and said that the TV noise 'drives me mad'.

Interview 110 (2) Married couple in their 50s, husband drove an earthmover. He'd had hearing problems for years. He'd bought a private aid three years before, at his wife's insistance, but had only worn it for one month. He'd been to the GP regularly to have his ears syringed before that. He reported that the commercial aid fitter had said he was only two tones above total deafness. He said not hearing conversation suited him, 'I'm a loner'. There was a lot of conflict between his wife and himself over his hearing, she complained of TV noise and the difficulty of conversation.

Interview 111 (1) A 58-year-old man (interviewed alone), retired from work after the removal of one lung. He'd previously been a welder in an aerospace factory for twenty-five years, felt noise at work was responsible for his quite considerable hearing loss. He only followed conversation if someone was facing him directly, never used the phone. He was waiting until he was 'stone deaf' to go for a hearing aid as he thought that was when they were worn. Arguments at home with wife and grown-up son about television noise and repetition.

Interview 112 (2) Married couple in their 50s, husband had taken early retirement as a progress controller. He'd had trouble with his hearing for twenty years, 'only wax though'. Consequently he had had his ears syringed every two years for twenty years. His main problem was conversation – 'deaf as a post' he said 'when I've got the wax'. Both he and his wife seemed unconcerned by it and he followed the conversation easily in the interview.

Interview 113 (2) Married couple in their 50s, one daughter away. The husband a development manager of a shopping centre, the wife a housewife with severe arthritis. He'd had hearing problems for three years 'due to wax' he thought, although he'd never been to the doctor. His wife said his hearing loss 'drives me mad', the TV noise and lack of conversation especially. He said he made 'more effort at work to hear, there was nothing to bother for at home'. He found conversation an effort socially and had to concentrate. It was obviously an area of conflict between husband and wife.

Interview 114 (2) Married couple in their 50s. The husband an architect, the wife a housewife. He had been given an aid four years before but never wore it because of the fear of it being seen: he was worried it was a sign of growing old. He worried about his hearing becoming worse especially about it being noticeable at work. His wife saw it (unusually) as less of a problem than he did; although she got irritable about the television noise. He said, about his hearing loss and it's effect on conversation, 'it's a bit like learning French, you miss a lot'.

Interview 115 (2) Married couple in their late 50s, husband a maintenance-fitter in the printing industry. Wife a part-time care assistant. The husband had had a hearing loss for fifteen years as a result of a noisy workplace, he thought. He seemed more aware of it than his wife who said she didn't really notice it much apart from the television noise. His son had first noticed that he missed conversation. In the interview the respondent was reasonable in one-to-one conversation but missed some talk when the wife was included. He's never consulted a GP about his hearing.

Interview 116 (2) Married couple in late 50s. The husband worked as a storeman in the Waterworks and the wife was at home. He had had a perforated eardrum 'from the war' and had previously worked on the roads using a compressor. Didn't know which of these had caused his hearing loss. He'd been given an aid eighteen months before but never wore it as he was too embarrassed to do so in case anyone noticed it, especially workmates. He'd been to the hospital eighteen years before about his hearing. The television was a problem at home otherwise they managed satisfactorily, they felt.

Interview 117 (1) A man in his late 50s, working as a foreman engineer in the boiler room of a large hospital. He was married with grown-up children but was interviewed alone. He'd had a hearing problem for thirty-six years and a lot of ear infections. He worried that his hearing was getting much worse, he 'dreaded' using the phone and felt he was reaching the point where he would *'have'* to do something about it and get a hearing aid. He had two pre-lingually deaf workmates but he 'avoided' them, his father had been hard-of-hearing and his wife had a hearing loss in one ear. They argued 'a lot' about their hearing problems.

Interview 118 (2) Married couple in early 50s. Three years ago the husband, a quantity surveyor, had started having a hearing problem. He was finding work a struggle because of it, but felt it wasn't bad enough to do anything about it. His wife and daughter felt he wasn't admitting how bad it was. His grandchild had 'glue ear' and the husband kept referring to the child's *'real'* problem with his hearing.

Interview 119 (1,1) A technician aged 59, working in an aeronautical engineering laboratory (very noisy). He was interviewed alone as he said he and his wife led separate lives. He thought his hearing problems (of two years' duration) got on her nerves and she complained of television noise and his loud voice. His workmates 'covered up' for him at work. He hadn't been to the doctor and would only go when 'every conversation was a problem'. Interviewed twice.

Interview 120 (1) A 58-year-old fitter in a toolmaking factory, noisy workplace. He'd had a hearing loss 'for years' which he blamed on noise at work. His mother had a hearing aid. He played bowls with the centre for the deaf's team and had two deaf workmates. He said his home life had improved since his children (in their 20s) had left home. As teenagers he found they made him irritable about his hearing as they 'whispered' amongst themselves a lot. One daughter was now training as a speech therapist and she was understanding, the other two, away at university, were better than they had been, but still not ideal. He was a cheerful man who enjoyed life, played a lot of sport, and felt he now accepted his hearing loss as 'Anno Domini', whereas previously he'd let it get him down.

Interview 121 (2) A motor mechanic aged 58 living with his elderly father who was hard-of-hearing. He said he didn't have a hearing problem really but marked himself down as slightly hard-of-hearing. His father noted him down as hard-of-hearing. On the whole no real problem and unconcerned by the possibility of any.

Interview 122 (2) A married couple, the husband a 53-years-old aeroengine fitter. He had had a hearing loss for twenty years caused by working in a noisy environment, he felt. His mother was elderly hard-of-hearing. He'd been several times to the work's doctor but got fed up because he only ever syringed his ears. He felt sure if 'someone looked, they'd find something there' as his ear felt permanently blocked.

Interview 123 (2) Married couple in their 50s. The husband a fitter; testing aerospace engines, a very noisy workplace. He'd had a perforated eardrum whilst in the Navy. He was very anxious about his deteriorating hearing, he'd been to the work's doctor and then to the nearby hospital to have his ears syringed and drops put in. The television noise was a very significant cause of tension with his family. His wife said they 'had headaches all the time' because of it.

Interview 124 (2) Married couple in their early 50s, no children. The husband had recently been made redundant from a job as an accounts clerk and was finding that hard to adjust to. He'd had a hearing loss for eight years and had been to the hospital (after several years of annual ear syringing) where he'd been told he had a 'trapped nerve' and nothing could be done. He was fearful about a future decline in hearing as he spent a lot of time working voluntarily for the hospital broadcasting service. He also had tinnitus. His wife, an audio-typist, found the television noise a problem and both felt sorry that 'nothing could be done'.

Interview 125 (2) Married couple in their early 50s. Husband a foreman in a foundry (noisy workplace). The husband denied he had a hearing problem in the questionnaire but said he missed things a lot and had to ask people to repeat themselves. He also had tinnitus. His wife said she was constantly repeating things and his daughter teased him a lot about his hearing. The husband's father had been deafened in the First World War and the wife's mother had been hard-of-hearing. Both felt their parents were very isolated. They both worked with born-deaf colleagues and were positive about this experience.

Interview 126 (2) Married couple in their 50s. The husband was a clerk and the wife a home help. They had two teenage children. The husband had been to hospital twelve years before because of his hearing and had been told that there was nothing wrong. He'd lost confidence since then as his hearing had got worse but he'd never been back. His mother was 'deaf' and his father had a work-related hearing loss from being a blacksmith. His children got annoyed with him about his hearing.

Interview 127 (2) Married couple in their 50s, husband a production section manager in a noisy soft-drinks factory. He'd had trouble with his hearing for several years – 'At last he's saying he can't hear' commented his wife. He was trying to lip-read, missed conversation during interview. He'd been to the work's doctor who'd said there was nothing wrong. His wife and he both said he got very irritable because of his hearing. They were very open about the problem they were having as a result of his hearing loss.

Interview 128 (2) Married couple in their late 50s, the husband a superintendant, said he had no real hearing problems, his wife said he just missed the phone sometimes. He said he tended 'to switch off' in meetings and conversations. He'd had wax in his ears and had them syringed and often got catarrh which meant he then did have 'painful deaf' ears.

Interview 129 (1) A 59-year-old transport manager in a noisy workplace with heavy lorries. This man had had problems hearing for five years. He went and had his ears syringed regularly at work but had not been to the GP. He felt he was the sort of person who was 'irritable anyway' when he said that he got annoyed about not hearing. He said he was 'too proud' to ever tell people when he was out. His mother had been deafened by a bomb during the war and his wife had trouble with her hearing.

References

Abberley, P. (1985) 'Policing Cripples', in *Social Theory and Physical Handicap*, University of Warwick Working Paper 1986, ch. 3, p. 20.

Alpiner, J.G. (1980) 'Aural Rehabilitation for Adults', in R.L. Schow, M.A. Nerbonne (eds) *Introduction to Aural Rehabilitation*, Baltimore: University Park Press.

Ashley, J. (1973) *Journey into Silence*, London: Bodley Head.

Ashley, J. (1985) 'A Personal Account', in H. Orlans (ed.) *Adjustment to Adult Hearing Loss*, San Diego: College Hill Press.

Ashley, P.K. (1985) 'Deafness and the Family', in H. Orlans (ed.) *Adjustment to Adult Hearing Loss*, San Diego: College Hill Press.

Baldwin, S. (1984) *The Costs of Caring: Families with Disabled Children*, London: Routledge & Kegan Paul.

Barker, R.G., Wright, B.A., Myerson, L., and Gonick, M.R. (1953) *Adjustment to Physical Handicap and Illness: A Survey of the Social Psychology of Physique and Disability*, New York: Social Science Research Council, Bulletin 55.

Bateson, G., Jackson, D., Haley, J., and Weakland, J. (1956) 'Towards a Theory of Schizophrenia', *Behavioural Science* 1: 251–64.

Beattie, J.A. (1981) 'Social Aspects of Acquired Hearing Loss In Adults', unpublished Ph.D. thesis, University of Bradford.

Beethoven, L. Van (1802) *Heiligenstadt Document*, Hamburg: Stadtbibliothek.

Berger, P.L. and Luckman, T. (1966) *The Social Construction of Reality*, Harmondsworth: Penguin.

Bion, W. (1960) *Experiences in Groups and Other Papers*, London: Tavistock Publications.

Birenbaum, A. (1970) 'On Managing a Courtesy Stigma', *Journal of Health and Social Behaviour* 11: 196–206.

Blaxter, M. (1976) *The Meaning of Disability: A Sociological Study of Impairment*, London: Heinemann.

Boswell, D.M., Jaehnig, W.B., and Mittler, P. (1975) 'A Handicapped Identity' in *The Handicapped Person in the Community*, Milton Keynes: Open University Press.

Breed, P.C.M., Van der Horst, A.P.J.M., and Mous, T.J.M. (1980) *Psycho-Social Problems in Suddenly Deafened Adolescents and Adults*, paper presented at the First International Congress of the Hard-of-Hearing, Hamburg, Hamburg: Deutscher Schwerhoringenbund.

Briggs, A. and Oliver, J. (eds) (1985) *Caring: Experience of Looking After Disabled Relatives*, London: Routledge & Kegan Paul.

Brooks, D.N. (1972) 'The Use and Disuse of Medresco Hearing Aids', *Sound* 6: 80–5.

Brooks, D.N. (1979) 'Counselling and Its Effect on Hearing Aid Use', *Scandanavian Audiology* 8: 101–7.

Brooks, D.N. (1981) 'Use of Postaural Aids by NHS Patients', *British Journal of Audiology* 15: 79–86.

Bunting, C. (1981) *Public Attitudes to Deafness*, London: Office of Population Censuses and Surveys.

Campling, J. (ed.) (1981) *Images of Ourselves*, London: Routledge & Kegan Paul.

Conrad ,R. (1979) *The Deaf Schoolchild: Language and Cognitive Function*, London: Harper & Row.

Cooke, J. (1984) 'You Can't Argue With Your Genes', *Observer*, 16 December: 36.

Cooper, S. (1978) 'Paranoid Psychosis and Late Hearing Impairment', in Montgomery, G. (ed.) *Deafness, Personality and Mental Health*, Edinburgh: Scottish Workshop Publications.

Cottin, R.H. (1973) 'Consequences sociales et professionelles de l'apparation chez l'adulte d'une sourdite profonde ou totale', *Re-educational Orthophonique* 11, 72: 310–32.

Cowie, R.I.D. and Douglas-Cowie, E. (1983) 'Speech Production in Profound Postlingual Deafness', in M.E. Lutman and M.P. Haggard (eds) *Hearing Science and Hearing Disorders*, London: Academic.

Cox, K.M. (1985) *Integration Psychologists With Special Needs* DECP Proceedings, Blackpool 1985.

Davis, F. (1963) *Passage through Crisis: Polio Victims and Their Families*, New York: Bobbs-Merril.

Davis, A.C. (1983) 'Hearing Disorders in the Population', in M.E. Lutman and M.P. Haggard (eds) *Hearing Science and Hearing Disorders*, London: Academic Press.

Denmark, J.C. (1969) 'Management of Severe Deafness in Adults' *Proceedings of the Royal Society of Medicine* 62: 965–7.

Dickinson, M. (1977) 'Rehabilitating the Traumatically Disabled Adult', *Social Work Today* 8, 28

Dingwall, R. (1976) *Aspects of Illness*, London: Martin Robinson.

Education Act (1981) London: HMSO.

Equal Opportunities Commission (1981) *Behind Closed Doors*, Manchester: EOC.

Equal Opportunities Commission (1982) *Who Cares for the Carers?* Manchester: EOC.

Ferguson, N. and Watt, J. (1980) 'Professionals and the Parents of Mentally Handicaped Children', *Bulletin of the British Psychological Society* 33; 59–60.

Finch, J. and Groves, D. (eds) (1983) *A Labour of Love: Women, Work and Caring*, London: Routledge & Kegan Paul.

Finkelstein, V. (1980) *Attitudes and Disabled People: Issues for Discussion*, New York: World Rehabilitation Fund.

Glass, L. (1985) 'Hearing Impairment and Ageing: some research issues in the next decade'. Paper presented at the 9th World Congress of the World Federation of the Deaf, Palermo, Italy.

Goffman, E. (1963) *Stigma: Notes on the Management of a Spoiled Identity*, Harmondsworth: Penguin.

Graham, H. (1983) *Caring, A Labour of Love*, in J. Finch and D. Groves, (eds) *A Labour of Love: Women, Work and Caring*, London: Routledge & Kegan Paul.

Haggard, M.P., Foster, J.R., and Iredale, F.E. (1981) 'Use and Benefit of Post-Aural Aids in Sensory Hearing Loss', *Scandanavian Audiology* 10: 45–52.

Haines, C.M. (1972) 'The Effects of Defective Hearing Upon the Individual as a Member of the Social Order', *Journal of Abnormal and Social Psychology* 22:151–6.

Haley, J. and Hoffman, L. (1967) *Techniques of Family Therapy*, New York: Basic Books.

Hannam, C. (1975) *Parents and Their Mentally Handicapped Children*, Harmondsworth: Penguin.

Harris, A.I., Cox, E., and Smith, C.R. (1971) *Handicapped and Impaired in Great Britain*, Pt 1, London: HMSO.

Harrison, S. (1975) 'Social Consequences of the Long term Medical Treatment of Children', unpublished thesis, University of York.

Hartmann, H. (1985) 'From the Point of View of the Parent', in *Awareness and Identity of the Hard of Hearing* 2nd International Congress of the Hard of Hearing, Hamburg.

Harvington, Lord (1983) 'The Partially Deaf, speech to the House of Lords, *Hansard*, Vol. 440, 69:1148–51.

Hedges, A. (1985) 'An Introduction to Qualitative Research' in R. Walker (ed.) *Applied Qualitative Research*, London: Gower.

Hegarty, S. and Pocklington, K. (1983) *Hearing Therapists in the NHS*, London: National Foundation for Educational Research.

REFERENCES

Heider, F. and Heider, G.M. (1941) 'Studies in the Psychology of the Deaf (No.2)', *Psychological Monographs* 53, no. 242.

Hewett, S. (1970) *Handicapped Children and their Families*, Nottingham: University of Nottingham Press.

Hunt, W.M. (1944) 'Progressive Deafness', *Laryngoscope* 54: 229–34.

Hunt, P. (1966) *Stigma: The Experience of Disability*, London: Chapman and Hall.

Hutton, C.L. (1983) 'Hearing Aid Wear Times for Planning and Intervention in Aural Rehabilitation', *Journal of Rehabilitation Audiological* 16: 182–201.

Hyde, M., Pattison, E., and Sherman, G. (1981) 'Survey of the Perceived Needs of Hearing Impaired Adults in Queensland', *Australian Journal of Audiology* 3: 5–10.

Ingalls, G.S. (1946) 'Some Psychiatric Observations on Patients with Hearing Defect', *Occupational Therapy and Rehabilitation* 25: 62–6.

Jackson. D. (1974) *Human Communication*, Palo Alto: Science and Behaviour Books.

Jeffreys, M., Millard, J.B., Hyman, M., and Warren, M.D. (1969) 'A Set of Tests for Measuring Motor Impairment in Prevalence Studies', *Journal of Chronic Diseases* 22: 303–19.

Kaplan, H. (1985) 'Benefits and Limitations of Amplification and Speech-reading for the Elderly', in H. Orlans (ed.) *Adjustment to Adult Hearing Loss*, San Diego: College Hill Press.

Kew, S. (1975) *Handicap and Family Crisis*, Bath: Pitman.

Kirk, J.T. and Miller, M.L. (1986) *Reliability and Validity in Qualitative Research*, London: Sage.

Knapp, P.H. (1948) 'Emotional Aspects of Hearing Loss', *Psychosomatic Medicines* 10: 203–22.

Kraepelin, E. (1915) 'Der verfolgungswahn der schwerhoringen', *Psychiatrie Auflage 8*, Band IV. Barth, Leipzig.

Kyle, J.G. (1985) 'Deaf People: Assessing the Community or the Handicap', *Bulletin of the British Psychological Society* 38: 137–41.

Kyle, J.G. and Wood, P.L. (1983) *Social and Vocational Aspects of Acquired Hearing Loss*, Final Report to MSC, School of Education Research Unit, University of Bristol.

Kyle, J.G. and Wood, P.L., and Jones, L.G. (1983) *Hearing Aid Use and Level of Support for People Who Become Deaf*, Final Report to Bristol and Weston Health Authority. School of Education Research Unit, University of Bristol.

Kyle, J.G. and Wood, P.L. (1984) 'Changing Patterns of Hearing Aid Use and Level of Support', *British Journal of Audiology* 18: 211–16.

Kyle, J.G. and Wood, P.L. (1985) 'Vocational Aspects of Acquired Hearing

Loss', *International Journal of Rehabilitation Research* 8(4): 425–34, Rheinstetten, West Germany.

Kyle, J.G., Jones, L.G. and Wood, P.L. (1985) 'Adjustment to Acquired Hearing Loss: A Working Model', in H. Orlans (ed.) *Adjustment to Adult Hearing Loss*, San Diego: College Hill Press.

Kyle, J.G. and Woll, B. (1985) *Sign Language: The Study of Deaf People and Their Language*, Cambridge: Cambridge University Press.

Langer, E.J. (1983) *The Psychology of Control*, London: Sage.

Lehman, R.R. (1954) 'Bilateral Sudden Deafness', *New York State Journal of Medicine* May: 1481–4.

Leith, L. von der (1972a) 'Experimental Social Deafness', Scandanavian Audiology 1: 81–7.

Leith, L. von der (1972b) 'Hearing Tactics', *Scandanavian Audiology* 1: 155–60.

Levine, E.S. (1960) *The Psychology of Deafness*, New York: Grune & Stratton.

Lewis, J.M., Beavers, W.R., Gossett, J., and Phillips, V.A. (1976) 'No Single Thread: Psychological Health in Family Systems', New York: Brunner/Mazel.

Lindow, V. (1986) 'The Social Consequences of Seeing a Psychiatrist'. Unpublished PhD thesis, University of Bristol.

Loeb, G.E. (1985) 'The Functional Replacement of the Ear', *Scientific American* 252, 2: 86–92.

Luey, H.S. (1980) 'Between Two Worlds: the Problems of Deafened Adults', *Social Work in Health Care* 5: 253–65.

Lysons, K. (1984) *Hearing Impairment: A Guide for People with Auditory Handicaps and Those Concerned with Their Care and Rehabilitation*, Cambridge: Woodhead-Faulkner.

McKnight, J. (1981) 'Professionalized Service and Disabling Help', in A. Brechin, P. Liddiard, and J. Swain (eds) *Handicap in a Social World*, London: Hodder & Stoughton.

Mahapatra, S.B. (1974a) 'Psychiatric and Psychosomatic Illness in the Deaf', *British Journal of Psychiatry* 125: 450–1.

Mahapatra, S.B. (1974b) 'Deafness and Mental Health: Psychiatric and Psychosomatic Illness in the Deaf', *Acta Psychiatrica Scandinavica* 50: 596–611.

Markides, A., Brooks, D.N. Hart, F.G., and Stephens, S.D.G. (1979) 'Aural Rehabilitation of Hearing-Impaired Adults' (official policy of the British Society of Audiology), *British Journal of Audiology* 13: 7–14.

Martineau, H. (1983) *Autobiography*, London: Virago. (First published 1877.)

Maurer, J.F. and Rupp, R.R. (1979) *Hearing and Ageing*, New York: Grune & Stratton.

Mead, G.H. (1934) *Mind, Self and Society*, Chicago: University of Chicago Press.

Meadow, K.P. (1980) *Deafness and Child Development*, Berkeley: University of California Press.

Meadow-Orlans, K.P. (1985) 'Social and Psychological Effects of Hearing Loss in Adulthood: A Literature Review', in H. Orlans (ed.) *Adjustment of Adult Hearing Loss*, San Diego: College Hill Press.

Menninger, K.A. (1924) 'The Mental Effects of Deafness', *Psychoanalytical Review* 11: 144–55.

Minuchin, S. (1974) *Families and Family Therapy*, London: Tavistock.

Myerson, L. (1948) 'Experimental Injury: An Approach to the Dynamics of Physical Disability', *Journal of Social Issues* 4: 68–71.

Mykelbust, H.R. (1964) *The Psychology of Deafness*, New York: Grune & Stratton.

Nett, E. (1960) *The Relationships between Audiological Measures and Handicap*, a project of the University of Pittsburgh School of Medicine and the Office of Vocational Rehabilitation, Washington: United States Department of Health, Education and Welfare.

Oliver, J. (1983) 'The Caring Wife', in J. Finch and D. Groves (eds) *A Labour of Love: Women, Work and Caring*, London: Routledge & Kegan Paul.

Oliver, M. (1981) 'Disability, Adjustment and Family Life', in A. Brechin, P. Liddiard, and J. Swain (eds) *Handicap in a Social World*, London: Hodder & Stoughton.

Orlans, H. and Meadow-Orlans, K.P. (1985) 'Responses to Hearing Loss: Effects on Social life, Leisure and Work, *Shhh*6(1): 4–7, Bethesda, Maryland.

Oyer, M.J. and Oyer, J.O. (1985) 'Adult Hearing Loss and the Family', in M. Orlans (ed.) *Adjustment to Adult Hearing Loss* San Diego: College Hill Press.

Parsons, T. (1951) *The Sociological System*, Glencoe: Free Press.

Peck, A.W., Samuelson, E.E., and Lehma, A. (1926) *Ears and the Man: Studies in Social Work for the Deaf*, Philadelphia: F. Davies.

Pederson, B., Frankner, B., and Terkildsen, K. (1974) 'A Prospective Study of Adult Danish Hearing Aid Users' *Scandanavian Audiology* 3: 107.

Phillips, G.B. (1973) 'Survey of Career Opportunities for the Deaf'. M.Ed. Dissertation, University of Rochester, New York.

Poster, M. (1978) *Critical Theory of the Family* London: Macmillan

Powell, J. and Rayne, J.W. (1952) *Progress Notes: Disaster Investigation*, Army Chemical Centre, Chemical Core Medical Laboratories, Edgware MD.

Ramsdell, D.A. (1962) 'The Psychology of the Hard-of-Hearing and Deafened Adult, in M. Davis and S.R. Silverman (eds) *Hearing and Deafness* New York: Holt, Rinehart & Winston.

Richtberg, W. and Bochnik, M.J. (1980) *On the Personal Situation of the Hard of Hearing and Those Who Become Deaf in Later Life*, paper presented to the First International Congress of the Hard of Hearing, Hamburg: Deutscher Schwerhoringenbund.

Ries, P.W., (1985) 'The Demography of Hearing Loss', in H. Orlans (ed.) *Adjustment to Adult Hearing Loss*, San Diego, California: College Hill Press.

Ronayne, T. and Wynne, R. (1985) 'The Stress Perspective and Hearing Disabled', Paper presented to Annual Association for the Deaf, Port Laoise.

Rupp, R., Higgins, J., and Maurer, J. (1977) 'A Feasibility Scale for Predicting Hearing Aid Use (FSPHAU) with Older Individuals', *Journal of the Academy of Rehabilitation Audiology* 10: 81–104.

Safilios-Rothschild, C. (1981) 'Disabled Persons' Self Definitions and Their Implications for Rehabilitation', in A. Brechin, P. Liddiard, and J. Swain, (eds) *Handicap in a Social World*, London: Hodder & Stoughton.

Schein, J.D. and Delk, M.T. (1974) *The Deaf Population of the USA*, Silver-springs: *National Association of the Deaf.*

Schlesinger, H.S. (1985) 'The Psychology of Hearing Loss', in H. Orlans (ed.) *Adjustment to Adult Hearing Loss*, San Diego: College Hill Press.

Schow, R. and Nerbonne, M. (eds) (1980) *Introduction to Aural Rehabilitation*, Baltimore: University Park Press.

Scott, R.A. (1966) 'The Selection of Clients by Social Welfare Agencies: The Case of the Blind', *Social Problems* 14

Scott, R. (1969) *The Making of Blind Men. A Study of Adult Socialization*, New York: Russell Sage.

Seligman, M.E. (1975) *Helplessness*, San Francisco: Freeman.

Shapiro, J. (1983) 'Family Reactions and Coping Strategies in Response to the Physically Ill or Handicapped Child: A Review', *Social Science and Medicine,*17: 913–31.

Shearer, A. (1981) *Disability. Whose Handicap?* Oxford: Blackwell.

Shears, L.M. and Jensema, C.J. (1969) 'Social Acceptability of Anomolous Persons', *Exceptional Children* 36: 91–6.

Stephens, S.D.G. (1977) 'Hearing Aid Use by Adults: A Survey of Surveys', *Clinical Otolaryngology* 2: 385–402.

Stephens, S.D.G. (1980) 'Evaluating the Problems of the Hearing Impaired', *Audiology* 19: 205–20.

Stone, H. (1985) 'Developing SHHH, a Self-Help Organisation', in H. Orlans (ed.) *Adjustment to Adult Hearing Loss.*

Thomas, D. (1982) *The Experience of Handicap*, London: Methuen.

Thomas, A.J. (1984) *Acquired Hearing Loss: Psychological and Psychosocial Implications*, London: Academic.

Thomas, A.J. and Herbst, K.G. (1980) 'Social and Psychological Implications of Acquired Deafness in Adults of Employment Age' *British Journal of Audiology* 14: 76–85.

Thomas, A.J., Lamont, M., and Harris, M. (1982) 'Problems Encountered at Work by People with Severe Acquired Hearing Loss', *British Journal of Audiology* 16: 39–43.

Thomas, D. (1978) *The Social Psychology of Childhood Disability*, London: Methuen.

Tomlinson, S. (1982) *Sociology of Special Education*, London: Routledge & Kegan Paul.

Townsend, P. (1973) *The Social Minority*, London: Allen Lane.

Trevains, S. (1982) *Acquired Hearing Loss and Employment Prospects*, Sheffield: BJM Research Partners Ltd for the MSC Employment Services Division.

Trychin, S. (1985) 'Stress Management', *Journal of Self-Help for Hard of Hearing* Sept./Oct.: 8–10, People Inc. Shhh, Bethesda, Maryland.

Voysey, M. (1975) *The Constant Burden: The Reconstitution of Family Life*, London : Routledge & Kegan Paul.

Ward, L. (1983) *People First:Developing Services in the Community* London: King's Hospital Fund.

Warnock, M. (1978) *The People with a Mental Handicap: Special Educational Needs*. Report of the Committee of Enquiry into The Education of Handicapped Children and Young People. Cmnd 7212. London: HMSO.

Warr, P., Cook, J., and Wall, T. (1979) 'Scales For Measurement of Some Work Attitudes and Aspects of Psychological Well-being', *Journal of Occupational Psychology* 52: 129–48.

Watts, A. (1983) *Acquired Deafness in Adults*, London: Croom Helm.

Weller, D.J. and Miller, P.M. (1977) 'Emotional Reactions of Patient, Family and Staff in Acute Care Period of Spinal Cord Injury', *Social Work in Health Care* 3.

Welles, H.H. (1932) *The Measurement of Certain Aspects of Personality Among Hard of Hearing Adults*, New York: Teachers' College, Columbia University.

West, P. (1979) 'An Investigation into the Social Construction and Con-sequences of the Label Epilepsy', unpublished Thesis, University of Bristol.

Winstanley, Lord (1983) Speech to the House of Lords, *Hansard*, Vol. 440, 69: 1154–8.

Wood, P.L. and Kyle, J.G. (1983) 'Hospital Referral and Family Adjustment in Acquired Deafness', *British Journal of Audiology* 17: 175–81.

Zeckel, A. (1950) 'Psychopathological Aspects of Deafness', *Journal of Nervous and Mental Disorders* 112: 337–40.

Name Index

Subject Index